Green L.

From.

Gene Bainbridge

Dec- 1 9 3 8

X 3
10°⁰

W9-DJP-476

82281A

2-7

DESTINY AND DISEASE IN MENTAL DISORDERS

With Special Reference to the Schizophrenic Psychoses

THOMAS W. SALMON MEMORIAL LECTURES

DESTINY *and* DISEASE *in* MENTAL
DISORDERS
by Dr. C. Macfie Campbell

In Preparation

PSYCHIATRY: 1935
by Dr. Wm. A. White

PSYCHOBIOLOGY
by Dr. Adolph Meyer

DESTINY AND DISEASE IN MENTAL DISORDERS

With Special Reference to the Schizophrenic Psychoses

•

By C. MACFIE CAMPBELL
PROFESSOR OF PSYCHIATRY
Harvard University

W· W· NORTON & COMPANY, INC.
Publishers, New York

Copyright, 1935, by

W. W. Norton & Company, Inc.
70 Fifth Avenue, New York

First Edition

Printed in the United States of America for the
Publishers by the Van Rees Press, New York

To
J. D. C.

CONTENTS

FOREWORD

THE PSYCHIATRIST, living an amphibian life, is forced to talk in terms of endocrine glands and brain localization at one time, at another time to discuss mental attitudes, religious beliefs, social behavior. He is faced not only with the disturbed behavior of individual organs, but also with the disconcerting behavior of the person as a social unit. The life history of the individual patient includes his reactions to environmental influences, privations, strains, as well as the reaction of his tissues to infective organisms and to variations in material supplies. In the complicated disabilities of man the psychiatrist requires now to use the instruments of precision and the categories of his medical colleagues, again to use methods and categories more adequate to the fullness of human nature.

The general tendency of medical investigation to penetrate ever more deeply into the minute details of the special systems has had its influence on the study of nervous and mental disorders.

The gains from this intensive research are obvious. At the same time there is some danger that the broader aspects of human life may be neglected, and that an abstract conception of the individual patient may result. The attempt to explain the personality of man by impersonal processes when carried too far may only result in explaining away personality.

Worship of the experimental method has unduly discredited the value of the painstaking analysis of the individual personality by the historical method. In the study of new growths, of infectious and nutritional disorders, the invaluable guinea-pig and his laboratory colleagues offer themselves as useful substitutes for the human individual. One gets much insight into the workings of human organs from the study of similar organs in these experimental animals. In its nutritive balance and resistance to infection the guinea-pig has much in common with man; as a personality the guinea-pig is limited. The problems associated with the inner conflicts of human nature and with the adaptation of the individual to his cultural environment with its historic background are but faintly adumbrated in the guinea-pig, still more faintly in the crustacean and the amoeba.

For insight into human personality and its disorders we must not look too exclusively to our humbler fellows in the animal kingdom. We must study man himself, man as he reacts in different ages and in different climes to the varied demands of cultural life, man with the fullness of his inner experience.

Man, however, is a refractory object for the study of the personality, owing to his complicated inhibitions and conventions; the experimenter, too, suffers from these same handicaps.

Thus the traditional body of psychological doctrine suffers from many gaps, reticences, misinterpretations; the human guinea-pig has been chary of exposing his inner works. This gap in our knowledge is largely the result of confining one's studies to the normal man, for the normality of an individual consists of a social adaptation sufficiently conventional to conceal from his fellows the workings of the deeper forces within his nature. The nature of these deeper forces can only be revealed when this conventional veil is torn aside. Thus the most valuable insight into the deeper forces of human nature is offered by nervous and mental patients; they present these forces in all their nakedness, or with transparent disguises. Much that disconcerts, perplexes, shocks us in the so-called abnormal is nothing new; it merely represents something which in the so-called normal is woven as an indistinguishable element into a complex texture within the framework of the personality.

In these lectures a brief account is given of many troubled lives, and an attempt is made to formulate them in terms of the human personality grappling with the special difficulties of its individual destiny. Such an account does not neglect the intensive study of the impersonal processes within the organism, but is meant to supplement such study; the aim is to place such detailed studies in the right perspective.

DESTINY AND DISEASE IN
MENTAL DISORDERS

*With Special Reference to the
Schizophrenic Psychoses*

I

TRENDS IN
PSYCHIATRY

MAKING allowance for the common tendency to attribute undue importance to the events of one's own times, much may still be said for the claim that during the first decades of this century psychiatry has done more than make steady progress along established lines, that it has to a large extent undergone a transformation.

The period of Dr. Thomas W. Salmon's professional life coincided with this period of psychiatric advance, and in a special manner he represented the very spirit of the progress and transformation of psychiatry. In the first few years of his professional activity he worked within the walls of the mental hospital; during his later years his field of work was the life of the community in general, he was occupied with problems in human relations brought to him from the most diverse sources. He had become the accredited representative of psychiatry to the medical profession and to the leaders in the field of social welfare. During his lifetime, and in large part due to his influence, the barriers which isolated the mental hospital from the medical profession and from the general community were breached, the specialized knowledge of the hospital physician became more freely available to the community, while the current of medical progress flowed more freely into the wards of the mental hospital.

During the nineteenth century the right of the insane to kindly care had been explicitly recognized, although it was only through prolonged effort in the face of passive opposition that this theoretical recognition was translated into practical measures. It was possible for Charles Reade in 1863 to publish *Hard Cash* with its lurid presentation of the treatment of mental patients which he claimed he could substantiate by documentary evidence. In 1908 Clifford Beers published a graphic account of his personal experiences during a prolonged attack of mental disorder, and in this account he faced the public and the medical profession with the challenge of mental disorders and with the facts of contemporary treatment. In 1917, in the first number of *Mental Hygiene,* Thomas W. Salmon published a poignant picture of the way in which mental patients were at that time being treated, or rather neglected, by a prosperous community apparently otherwise responsive to the needs of a wholesome cultural life. These data remind us of the neglect and prejudice in relation to mental disorders which tend to persist as a continuing background, notwithstanding the striking progress in investigative and therapeutic work on which we prefer to focus attention.

The nineteenth century not only acknowledged the right of the insane to humane care; it also saw the medical profession accept mental disorders as topics of systematic investigation and teaching on an equal footing with the diseases with which general medicine dealt. The early attack on these problems was carried out under the domination of pathological anatomy, and the century closed with a creditable record of advance in our knowledge of the structure of the brain and of the detailed changes in the parenchyma and supporting structures in a variety of morbid conditions. With regard to the great majority of patients called insane, their behavior, their subjective experience, their beliefs, remained as mysterious as before; the industrious clinician could only study the external manifestations and the evolution of these disorders, and analyze the individual clinical picture to the best of his ability in the light of the current psychology of the period.

Before the century finished a new movement of fundamental importance had been initiated, which was to have a profound influence on the whole evolution of psychiatric thought. Sigmund Freud, beginning with studies on hysteria, had revealed the importance of unconscious factors in the structure of the personality; he had put forth the view that not only hysterical and compulsive symptoms, but also ideas of reference, hallucinatory voices and visual images, might have their origin in repressed tendencies and memories. In 1896 he had already published the presentation of a schizophrenic psychosis as an attempted adaptation of the personality to inner conflicts.

At the beginning of the present century the full implication of the new formulations of the personality was far from being realized. Explanations of disturbed behavior and outlook were industriously sought through the detailed study of impersonal factors, and the fruits of histopathological study were much in the foreground. Nissl had finally arrived at a precise formulation of the histopathological picture in general paralysis; the changes in other forms of cerebral lues, in cerebral vascular disease, in senile degeneration, were differentiated from each other. New technical methods were being elaborated and it was hoped that these methods might reveal structural changes not previously demonstrated and thus throw light on the more baffling mental disorders. The optimistic hopes of some for quick returns were, however, not to be realized, and the clinician still awaits from the histopathologist an authoritative interpretation of his contribution to some of the most vexing problems in psychiatry.

While pathological anatomy was of value in demonstrating the structural changes underlying certain disorders and in supplying criteria for the establishment of homogeneous groups of cases, it left the fundamental problems of even these disorders to be investigated by other methods. It could demonstrate the characteristic histopathological changes in general paralysis and could finally track the spirochaete to its lair, but the further analysis of the disease was a matter for the clinician with the assistance of the physiologist, the biochemist, the protozoölogist. So the histopathological differentiation of the brain changes in vascular disorders, in chronic alcoholism, in senile psychoses, prepared the ground for a more intensive study of the several processes involved in these conditions. In the con-

vulsive disorders the histopathological study of
the brain might in perhaps half the cases contribute data of some value for the formulation
of the disorder; in the other cases the whole
burden of interpretation had to be based on data
derived by other methods.

For the understanding of the impersonal
mechanisms underlying abnormal human behavior, psychiatry received important aid from
the elucidation of other diseases. Disorders of
motility, hyperkinetic and akinetic conditions,
anomalous postures and gestures, were illuminated
by the increasing knowledge of the functions of
the lower centers. Wilson's pioneer work on the
lenticular nucleus, the analysis of the changes in
the striatum in Huntington's chorea, in Syden-
ham's chorea and in Parkinson's disease, the
lessened initiative or marked motor drive in epi-
demic encephalitis, offered suggestions for the
interpretation of disorders of motility in mental
patients. Experimental work (DeJong and H.
Baruk) showed that it was possible to produce
in animals by a drug (bulbocapnine) or by an
organismal toxin (colon bacillus toxin) motor disorders and postures strikingly similar to those observed in mental patients. As with the production,
so with the removal of certain motor symptoms;

experiments with patients demonstrated the rapid relaxation of muscular rigidity as well as the temporary cessation of mutism on the administration of certain drugs (CO_2, sodium amytal).

The light thrown on motility disorders by the study of the striatum has been no more illuminating than the results of the investigation of the hypothalamic region. The collaboration of neurosurgeon, neuroanatomist, neurophysiologist, revealed the importance of this region for various functions which concern the psychiatrist—the emotional reactions, the basal metabolism, the fat metabolism, the regulation of temperature, the sleep rhythm—giving a new significance to familiar anomalies of weight, sleep and emotional reaction, with perhaps the temptation to the clinician to translate his actual observations into a neurophysiological formula more precise than the exact state of our knowledge justifies. These investigations gave to the familiar descriptive terms a much fuller connotation than they previously had; the term emotion was no longer the symbol for a mere subjective experience, nor adequately covered by the James-Lange formula, but connoted in addition to the subjective experience the complicated pattern of autonomic, endocrine and diencephalic reactions outlined by Cannon. The hedonistic or pleasure-pain quality of experience could be thought of in terms of a possible thalamic component; the clinical description of the feeling-tone of the patient had implicit in it a reference to the autonomic nervous system, however elusive the rôle of the latter might prove to the investigator. The combined data of many investigators brought before the psychiatrist the important rôle of humoral influences in relation to the well-being of the individual, the play of his feelings and emotions, the shifting output of his energy. It might not be easy in the individual case of mental disorder to analyze the respective contributions of the various physiological components; the basal metabolism might be low, the acid-base equilibrium disturbed, the sensitivity of the respiratory center anomalous, while the underlying cause remained obscure.

Physiology did not limit itself to the study of special systems in isolation from the rest of the organism. It also studied experimentally the modes of reaction of the animal as a whole, and the way in which the experience of the animal modifies its later reactions. Pavlov studied with great precision the reaction of dogs to stimuli originally neutral, which had acquired a special significance for the animal in the light of its individual experience. In the varied reactions of his dogs to a certain sequence of stimuli he saw an analogy with the classical temperaments. Conditions somewhat similar to the nervous disorders of man could be produced by suitable variation of environmental stimuli; for example, a state of marked irritability with loss of capacity for inhibition (neurasthenia), on the other hand a state of marked inhibition under the influence of strong stimuli (hysteria), and such schizophrenic symptoms as negativism and stereotypy. Pavlov drew an analogy between schizophrenic patients and his experimental animals, and suggested that schizophrenia might be looked on as a state of chronic hypnosis or inhibition, an adaptive reaction for the protection of the cortical cells. Whatever the validity of such analogies may be, such experiments at least show that under even very simple conditions striking symptoms may be developed, which are not to be explained merely in localizing structural terms but in the light of the past experiences of the individual.

As one may concentrate on the component systems and functions in the study of the symptomatology of mental disorders, so in regard to the causative factors some devote attention exclusively to those impersonal factors which play the main rôle in the general field of medicine. The factors which in a mental disorder upset the balance of the organism and disturb the system of forces called the personality may be of comparatively simple nature. A physical concussion may be sufficient; undue exposure to sunshine may bring about a like result. The crucial factor may be the inadequate supply of some material essential for the system, as in the pellagrous psychoses. In other cases the disorder of the personality may be due to some poison introduced from without. The insidious effect of infection has to be reckoned with, although its demonstration requires expert and critical evaluation. The gastro-intestinal tract has been incriminated as the source of toxic substances, but extraordinary technical difficulties stand in the way of the adequate systematic study of the flora of the gastro-intestinal tract.

It is obvious that research in many fields has brought to the psychiatrist important data bearing on human behavior, which he is bound to utilize in the scrutiny and interpretation of his clinical material. The data are obviously incomplete; there are still alarming gaps in our knowledge, and what is tentative and hypothetical is not always separated from what is soundly established.

The prestige attached to research dealing with the impersonal processes of disease leads some to hold that further progress in psychiatric investigation must await advances in the basal sciences. It is dangerous, however, for psychiatry to take this dependent attitude towards the solution of its special problems and to demand too much from other disciplines. Psychiatry has its own special problems which have to be dealt with by appropriate methods. The behavior and inner experience of the individual cannot be adequately studied by any method of analysis which does not take into account the nature of man. Human nature cannot be adequately analyzed by the methods of chemistry and physiology and general biology.

The methods of investigation which we have been describing are appropriate for the study of the vegetative life, for the general dynamics of the organism, for the affective reactions, for the simpler aspects of the life of external relations, for the ability of the organism to react to comparatively simple patterns of stimuli as in Pavlov's dogs. The nature of the individual patient, however, with whom the physician has to deal, is not altogether exhausted by reference to these factors in his composition. The individual patient has a need of self-expression, a need for the construction of a world with both a physical and a moral order, a need for a personal feeling of value. In the total system of forces which make up the human organism and the human personality one has to do justice to *thought,* that complex system of symbolizing activity by means of which the individual grasps the external world and brings it within manageable compass.

These are characteristics of the individual patient and are an essential element in the actual unit with which the psychiatrist has to deal. One may discard these factors, refuse to take clinical cognizance of them, concentrate on the physiological aspects of the situation, and hope that thereby one may arrive at some conclusions of practical value. We have no guarantee, however, that in discarding these aspects of the actual situation we may not be putting aside factors which are essential for understanding the practical problems before us. The failure to arrive at a satisfactory solution of our problems by the methods of biochemistry and physiology may be due not to the lack of advancement of these sciences but to the fact that these methods are inadequate for the task of psychiatry.

Noteworthy expression was given to this point of view by Adolph Meyer when he published in

1906 his *Fundamental Conceptions of Dementia Praecox,* followed in 1909 by his paper on *The Dynamic Interpretation of Dementia Praecox.* These papers and the personal teaching of Meyer had a profound influence on the direction of psychiatric thought in America, and their wholesome and steadying influence is one of the great assets of American psychiatry. Meyer emphasized the necessity in the study of patients of taking into account not only the somatic functions but also the more specifically human functions, of taking account of the way in which the individual actually deals with the concrete problems of life, of paying attention to the complex functions which under stress or strain may give rise to emotional disturbance, thought disorder, perplexing anomalies of conduct, of recognizing the special vulnerability of certain types of personality. The individual case has to be studied as an example of human nature in difficulty, and in this analysis of human nature there is no justification for confining oneself to physiological categories.

The publication in 1907 of C. G. Jung's *Psychology of Dementia Praecox* brought a powerful reënforcement to the view that the individual psychosis must be considered not as merely symptomatic of an impersonal disease process but as part of the adaptation of a human individual to the special demands of his inner nature and of the environmental situation. Jung reviewed the various symptoms of dementia praecox in the same way in which he had come to review the symptoms of hysteria under the influence of Freud, and he drew a striking parallel between dementia praecox and hysteria. He compared the structure of the dream with that of the mentality of the dementia praecox patient: "The dreamer finds himself in a new and different world which he has projected from himself. If we allow a dreamer to go about and behave like one awake we shall have the clinical picture of dementia praecox." In his study of an old case of paranoid dementia he showed how beneath neologisms and dilapidated utterances there might be the familiar needs and desires of human nature.

Clinical psychiatry had for too long studied the individual clinical picture as a mosaic of symptoms. It had discussed the various patterns of these mosaics and analyzed in a formal way the component elements, the disorders of mood, of thought, of perception, of volition, but it had failed to study them in the setting of the adaptation of the individual to the demands of his environment. From now on the clinical picture ceased to be a mosaic of symptoms and became a problem in human adaptation. This adaptation was something more than the physiological adaptation to the fundamental tasks of the organism; it was the personal adaptation to the demands of a cultural environment. Even with the simpler adaptive functions intact, the demands of the environment might be beyond the capacity of the individual; maladaptations might occur even although the methods of internal medicine disclosed no somatic ailment. The fact that an organism was competent to deal with its simpler chemical and organismal problems was no guarantee that it was competent to deal with the demands of the social environment, and the latter ability could only be estimated by studying in detail the life experience of the individual, his reaction to the specific conditions of his life, to prolonged situations and to episodic strains. It might not be possible to measure the resistance of the individual and his adaptability in the same precise terms as one could measure the organismal immunity of the individual, his reaction to muscular exercise or to the ingestion of sugar, but this lack of precision had to be accepted as determined by the very nature of the problem.

The study of the psychosis as a problem in human adaptation was the study of the individual personality with its own life history and life situation, and the personality came to occupy the center of the psychiatric stage. As in the production of an infectious disease the specific noxa may be made responsible, or on the other hand the lack of immunity of the patient, so in mental disorder we may emphasize the external factors which break down the resistance of the patient or the inadequate immunity of the patient. The estimate of the immunity of the personality was the task of the psychiatrist, and in estimating this psycho-immunity the psychiatrist had to weigh the significance of the family history, the moulding influence of early situations, the sensitizing or immunizing result of special experiences, the subtle internal evolution and adjustment of the component forces of the personality, the intimate interplay between the personality of the patient and the other personalities with which he was in close contact. The so-called psychosis, the problem of the psychiatrist, was this system of forces at a particular phase of its evolution studied in the setting of a particular situation.

In the analysis of the human personality, whether in a period of psychosis or apart from a psychosis, the contribution of Freud and his pupils was of the greatest importance. Freud had emphasized the great importance of the system of repressed forces called the unconscious; he had emphasized the symbolic expression of repressed factors in dream and in neurotic symptom; he had called attention to the early manifestations and the far-reaching significance of the sex life and of various pleasure-seeking tendencies; he had emphasized the persistence in adult life of repressed childhood tendencies of which the individual himself might not be conscious. The psychosis or the adaptation of the psychotic individual to the life situation was not the adaptation of a schematized personality of conventional type, it was the reaction of this real system of forces; its complicated components only to be adequately surveyed with a great expenditure of time. The personality could not be resolved into a series of physiological factors, nor be adequately studied by a mere survey of the overt traits and reactions; it had to be grasped as a very complex system of forces which bore within it the traces of its early conditioning. The analysis of the individual personality meant the careful and unusually detailed reconstruction of a life history.

The interest of the psychiatrist in the systematic classification of cases was thus to a large extent supplanted by interest in studying the dynamic problem of the individual case and in considering anew the possibilities of treatment and prevention. In the system of forces of the personality only a provisional delimitation for practical purposes of investigation could be made between biochemical, physiological and psychological factors, which represented the abstract components of a completely integrated individual. Psychiatry considered as its field disorders of the personality and felt entitled to deal with the individual case by whatever method was appropriate; it sought in the individual case to attribute its due value to each of the many component factors, biochemical, physiological, psychological, environmental. It had to accept responsibilty for studying and treating both coöperative and non-coöperative patients, cases where continuous and accurate observation was possible, and cases where observations had to be fragmentary and lacking in precision.

In this whole field it could separate cases where the most important practical question lay at the physiological level, others where it concerned the internal balance of the personality, others again where the environmental situation was of considerable importance. Psychiatry was willing to utilize any methods which might help to throw light upon its task and to incorporate any data which were well established. In the general field of psychiatry one group confined itself very largely to problems at the level of the personality, leaving to others the investigation of the more detailed physiological functions and of the life situation with its special complexities. The psychoanalytic school occupied itself almost exclusively with the treatment of a highly selected group of patients presenting special forms of mental disorder, whose symptoms allowed prolonged coöperation with the physician. The prolonged and intensive study of the individual patient by this school brought very valuable data to psychology, and in many cases was of therapeutic benefit to the patient. From the point of view of the clinical psychiatrist, psychoanalytic doctrines insofar as they were valid belonged to the body of knowledge included under psychology and psychopathology; the psychoanalytic method insofar as it was a therapeutic procedure was one form of psychotherapy.

The dominating trend in psychiatry under the influences referred to became the emphasis on the personality, and on the conception of the psychosis as the revelation of the personality grappling with its special tasks. The problem of the psychiatrist was no longer to identify a clinical picture but to get to grips with the actual dynamic situation, to reconstruct in detail the life history, with attention to the sensitizing or conditioning influence of environmental factors, and with due appreciation of the nature of emotional disturbances, of substitutive and evasive reactions, of symbolic expressions, of the various modes of getting satisfaction for the complicated needs of the individual.

In such a review due attention had also to be paid to any physiological inadequacies, any lack of essential supplies, the presence of any noxious substances, but these latter factors had to be seen in proper perspective and without neglect of the more complex functions of the personality.

The human personality is a complex system and there are many ways of approaching its analysis. The personality may be characterized through analysis of the total behavior and inner experience into a number of component reactions or traits. The exact formulation of these traits is not an easy matter, and the criteria for rating the degrees of any individual trait are difficult to establish. One may mention, for example, two such traits as sensitiveness, seclusiveness; these traits indicate important qualities of the personality in regard to the plasticity and efficiency of adaptation to the exigencies of life, but a precise estimate of the quality in the individual case is not possible.

Jung offered as a framework for the analysis of the personality a schema of psychological types, based on the systematic and profound analysis of a rich clinical material, and Kretschmer emphasized the principle that certain psychological types with their special attitudes to life are correlated with physical characteristics equally determined by the native endowment of the individual.

While some investigators of the personality concentrated on the analysis of adult patients and on the detailed reconstruction of their development, and others controlled such data by actual observations of the infant and child, Rüdin and his fellow-workers emphasized the basic contribution of the genetic endowment to the structure of the personality.

In the analysis of the personality not only was it necessary to consider the stock which had given to the individual his specific genetic endowment and to scrutinize the various stages of the individual's development with due attention to environmental influences; it was also necessary to take account of the modes of behavior and the beliefs prevalent in the infancy of the race, and liable to make a

transitory appearance in childhood. The study of
the reactions and formulations of adult patients,
as of the dreams of normal and abnormal individuals, revealed in the adult traces not only of
childhood tendencies but of the tendencies and
formulations of primitive man. Primitive tendencies and beliefs are present both in the normal
and the abnormal, and play a considerable part in
modern culture. They permeate the mores of the
group. They are deeply interwoven into the structure of language. They play an important rôle in
art and in religion. The old attitude of man
towards the planets indicated by the word *disaster*
has not disappeared without leaving its trace;
under suitable circumstances it still expresses itself, and many a patient feels that between him
and the planets there is an important interchange
of forces. In the sacraments of modern religion
we see a new version of early totem feasts. In
the holidays of the Christian calendar we have
the continuation of many old-time pagan festivals.
Magical practices and beliefs are still widely dis-
seminated in our modern community, and beneath
many an apparently jesting procedure there is a
serious driving force.

Among the symptoms of mental disorders occur
elements which have their source in the archaic

stratum of the mind, and in order to learn something of this stratum psychiatry has borrowed heavily from the anthropologist. The psychiatrist finds that the *Golden Bough* may throw light upon ideas and behavior of his patient which otherwise would remain hopelessly obscure. The extent to which primitive modes of thought are recapitulated in the experience of the child has been illustrated by Piaget in his book on *The Child's Conception of the World*.

The general trend of psychiatric thought and procedure led naturally to increased interest in the human personality in other settings than that of the clinic. The knowledge of the personality derived from the clinic was valid for the personality in all human relations, and psychiatry stepped outside the clinic to survey the field of human relations in general. If it occasionally made its approach to new fields with something of a propagandist attitude, it was also with an inquiring spirit and it thereby enriched its experience. The boundary between the normal and the abnormal was for its inquiry into personality quite irrelevant, but its first approach was to those situations where trouble of some sort existed, in the home, in the school, in the court, in industry. By this time it was ready to pass into general society, and to find material for observation in the ordinary walks of life, in social and political activities, in literature and on the stage.

The analysis of the adult personality had shown the importance of the original pleasure-seeking tendencies of the child for the formation of the later personality, and had revealed the persistence of these tendencies and of childhood modes of thought beneath the surface of the adult personality. The direct study of the personality of the child became a matter of importance for psychiatry, and the material supplied by psychologists and teachers was eagerly welcomed. It was not the contributions that dealt with such topics as special skills or the learning process that were of special value, but those dealing with the instinctive and emotional life of the child, with his gropings for satisfaction and for a grasp of the outside world, and with his urge towards self-expression. Tantrums, night-terrors, bed-wetting, sexual groping, capriciousness with regard to food, wayward behavior, became the subject of careful scrutiny; the complexity of the forces involved in the interrelation of child with parents and siblings began to be more generally recognized. The observation of infants and children in child-guidance clinics, nursery schools, and clinics, furnished a

wealth of data with regard to the behavior of the
child, while observations such as those of Piaget
threw fresh light on the child's attitude to the outside world.

The child himself might show the need of
psychiatric attention in view of special behavior,
attitude or complaints, although there was some
difference of opinion as to who should carry on the
psychiatric study and treatment. The pediatrist
with some reason claimed this to be his province,
but perhaps showed a rather undue sensitiveness
to "the menace of the psychiatrist."

Of those interested in the psychology and
psychopathology of childhood, the psychoanalysts
were among the most eager, and inspired by
Freud's presentation of *Der kleine Hans* and
Jung's account of *Anna* they plunged deeply into
the mysteries of the child's mind, sometimes with
more zeal than discretion, bringing up from
the depths material of rather uncertain origin.
To other workers the intensive or even direct examination of many a child seemed undesirable, as
the perplexing behavior or moods described
seemed to be only one element in a total family
situation, the management of which was the outstanding problem. The futility of studying the individual as an isolated unit, instead of as an

integral part of a social group, was less easy to overlook in the case of the child than in that of the adult.

Psychiatry as it looked round the home gathered valuable information with regard to the varieties of human personality, and with regard to the influence on the individual of personal relations and of the total situation. It saw many opportunities for therapeutic and preventive activity, although the professional medium of that help might be the teacher, the family doctor, the district nurse, the welfare worker.

Psychiatry was not content to limit its interest in the child to its development within the home and to the interplay between the personality of the child and that of the other members of the family group. It followed the child into the first important community organization to which every child is exposed, the school. Here, too, the problems with which the psychiatrist was first confronted were the more obvious evidences of maladaptation, indications of disharmony within the personality of the child, of unsatisfied desire for self-expression, for status and affection, indications of difficulty of the personality in adapting itself to the atmosphere of the schoolroom and the playground, to the discipline of authority, to

the requirements of social life. In the new setting
with its own special requirements and opportunities the personality received an important conditioning and the special problems peculiar to this
period offered an interesting field for investigation
and for therapeutic measures. Here, too, as in
the home, the solidarity of the individual with the
group had to be kept in mind; the study of
the child meant the study of a total situation with
special concentration on the system of the individual personality within the wider constellation.
Therapeutic efforts might be directed to modify-
ing the balance of the individual personality or
they might be chiefly directed towards the modification of the total situation.

These same principles were seen to be as valid
in the college as in the school. The individual has
in college to face new problems of adaptation, to
make further steps in emancipation and in self-
regulation, to deal with instinctive problems that
are frequently of great urgency, to emancipate
himself not only from dependence on persons but
from dependence on second-hand creeds and codes
and philosophies, and out of the traditional
material supplied he has to weave a living gar-
ment for his own personality. The problems of
adolescence and of early adult life are a further

test of the resistance of the personality to external strains and of the ability of the personality to develop its native endowment and to utilize environmental resources for its own purposes. A college may consider itself as more than a scholarly department store, it may recognize that it is an arena where the individual can exercise and train himself for life; with this attitude the college may hold it of importance to have available some trainers not concerned with the specialized skill of scholarship, but experienced in recognizing and dealing with faulty habits, inner conflicts, undigested experiences, second-rate and evasive adaptations.

Psychiatry, having followed the child into school and college, also followed the individual when his career brought him into contact with another social institution, the court. The traditional procedure of the court had paid little attention to considerations of personality, but had disposed of the problems of behavior in a somewhat rigid way according to the statutes. These latter had taken little cognizance of the individual personality, but had been formulated as a necessary safeguard for the welfare of the group. The growing recognition of the inadequacy of these rigid procedures made the court welcome the contribution which psychiatry was able to make to the fulfilment of its tasks. The judge had begun to realize that to ignore the personal factors in the individual case was an anachronism, but his legal training had offered him no help in analyzing or dealing with the personal factors involved. To psychiatry the misbehavior, which was the problem before the court, was only one special example of human adaptation and its study had to be carried on in the same way as that of other examples of human adaptation, in the same way in which one analyzed the compulsion of a nervous invalid, the truancy of a schoolboy, the tantrums of a child, the pedantry of a scholar. To this field, therefore, psychiatry made its important contribution, although the individual psychiatrist might not always realize that there were other factors to be considered in the total situation beyond those with which he was accustomed to deal under the categories of his medical work.

Conscious of the contribution which it could make, psychiatry may sometimes have had the appearance of pushing her wares and going beyond her province. The pediatrist might feel mildly resentful of the intrusion of the psychiatrist; the teacher might feel that he was perfectly competent through his intuition and his experience with youth to deal adequately with its disciplinary problems; the judge might feel inclined to demur when told that all delinquency should be regarded as a symptom of illness; but in these various spheres of human activity psychiatry established her definite place, and the individual psychiatrist carried on his special work as a member of a group working towards important social goals.

In other fields of human endeavor, such as in industry and in public affairs, the data and methods of psychiatry have been of value, although not necessarily employed by psychiatrists. Carleton Parker in his *The Casual Laborer and Other Essays* found the most profitable approach to this study through familiarity with the work of the clinical psychiatrist. He saw the behavior of the thwarted laborer as most suitably formulated in psychiatric terms. The laborer balked in the satisfaction of fundamental human needs, with no source of satisfaction in his work, no wholesome outlet for his human need of self-expression, develops "a condition of mental stress and unfocussed psychic unrest, which could in all accuracy be called a definite *industrial psychosis.*" For a diagnosis of this industrial psychosis Parker insists that one must know "the innate potentialities and inherited propensities of man," the human personality.

Dr. V. V. Anderson, working in a large department store, found that a large percentage of the employees were suffering from disorders of the personality which were best met by the procedure of a simple psychiatric review. The efficiency and general suitability of the worker were not to be evaluated merely by reviewing physical health, intellectual endowment, and special skill, but also in the light of the total personality and of the relations of the worker with the extra-occupational environment, the home and the social group.

Professor Elton Mayo has devoted special attention to the personal factors which are of importance in industry generally. On the basis of exact observations he has shown the relation between lowered productivity and increased labor turnover on the one hand, and on the other hand underlying feelings of depression and resentment which accumulate when the conditions of work fail to satisfy the requirements of human nature. In his interesting review of a prolonged experiment at the Hawthorne Plant of the Western Electric Company he calls attention to the very striking benefit to the morale of the workers derived from simple interviews, in which the individual worker had an opportunity of pouring out his views to a disinterested interviewer on any topics uppermost in his mind. The valuable result of this simple human contact is of great interest and must be taken into account when evaluating the results of an intensive and prolonged human contact such as is involved in psychotherapeutic treatment. The interviewing experiment emphasized the fact that the individual could not be adequately dealt with as an isolated unit, and that his efficiency was to a certain extent a function of the total situation including the group relationship.

In industry, as with the child in the home and the pupil in the school, the study of the isolated individual is the study of an abstraction. This dependence of the individual upon the culture in which he is living has great practical significance, and in problems of prevention one has to keep in mind not only the factors immediately relating to the individual himself but also the broader factors which are involved in the cultural environment.

With the increasing prevalence of these views the old economic unit of John Stuart Mill faded into the limbo of abstractions, and the economist began to recognize in the individual worker such factors as joy in work, the desire for self-expression, for prestige, for power and mutual helpfulness. In Paul H. Douglas's "The Reality of Non-Commercial Incentives in Economic Life" (in *The Trend of Economics,* edited by R. G. Tugwell) one finds the economist paying due tribute to the complex endowment of human nature.

Not only the economist and the sociologist but the student of political life has found psychiatry an aid to the solution of some of his problems. Lasswell in his study of political life (*Psychopathology and Politics*) feels it necessary to study the qualities of the human personality in the leaders, and finds "the richest body of psychological and sociological facts in the files of the institutions for the care of the mentally disordered." The same type of examination which the psychiatrist utilizes for clinical purposes is of value to the political scientist in studying the underlying determinants of the politician's behavior and beliefs.

The importance of the analysis of the human personality has led to the penetration of psychiatric methods and data into the field of interest of those working in the most diverse fields, and in some cases to the actual introduction of the

psychiatrist into the special field. It has even led
psychiatry into the field of general medicine, into
the general hospital, even into those on the pro-
spectus of which there was inscribed "no mental
cases admitted." It is gradually being realized that
a very large number of patients in general hospitals are mental patients, in the sense that their
handicap or disability cannot be adequately studied
or interpreted until one takes into account the
individual personality and the personal situation.

In many cases the nature of the symptoms is
only intelligible when they are seen as an element
in a pattern of emotional reaction or as one element in the adaptation to a personal situation.
Functional anomalies of individual systems and
organs may be due to the influence on the somatic
functions of subtle personal attitudes not con-
sciously realized. In some cases the severity and
duration of symptoms can only be understood
when due attention is paid to the personality and
the situation. At the present moment cases of
hyperthyroidism, of cardio-vascular disorder, of
gastric ulcer are being scrutinized to see how far
the disturbance of the special systems is a partial
manifestation of repressed elements in the instinctive and emotional life.

In the personality problems of the general hospital the affective life of the patient, his output of energy and the behavior of the individual organs and systems are in the foreground of attention. The symbolizing activity of the organism, by which it adapts itself to the external world and maintains its equilibrium, and which is so important for the mastery of the outside world, comes less under scrutiny. In the patients of the general hospital there is a recognition of sickness, an appeal for help, coöperation with the physician. With such coöperation disorders of comparatively simple nature, open to methods of precision and to experimentation, offer an attractive field for the psychiatrist, and there is some danger that his interest be diverted from the more perplexing problems of maladaptation where the thought processes are disturbed, where the patient's view of the outside world is strange and unintelligible, where the patient has no recognition of sickness and reaches out for no help from the physician but rather resents the latter's attempt to enter his charmed world and read its riddle.

The escape of psychiatry from the narrow field of mental disorders into the broader field of human activities, its excursion into the home, the school, the factory, the market place and the legislative assembly and into the wards of the general hospital, not only led to useful contributions to these special fields but also enriched the data of psychopathology. It broadened the insight of the psychiatrist into the way in which man deals with his problems, and into the diversity of human endowment and adaptation and total career. It emphasized the solidarity of the individual with the group, the bearing of the social background on the disordered mentality of the individual patient. It demonstrated that the methods and principles of psychiatry have validity in the study of human behavior in many settings where the question of disease is quite irrelevant. Thus psychiatry returned to its original material, freed from the incubus of the disease concept, willing to study the psychosis as an individual problem in human behavior.

It would do scant justice to the trends in psychiatry if one were to confine one's review to methods of investigation, to attempts at interpretation, and did not refer to the relation of these trends to the goal of all this professional activity, namely, treatment—the restoration of personal efficiency, the salvage from human shipwreck, the prevention of unnecessary disaster. To talk of the goal as the cure and prevention of disease would be to use too narrow a formula; it would fail to do justice to the complexity of the task and its true nature. Even in general medicine the *cure* of a disease through the intervention of the physician is not to be lightly claimed. The physician may have assisted in the temporary restoration of the equilibrium of the organism; he may have found that the supply of some definite substance would supplement the inadequacy of the organism, as in hypothyroidism, diabetes, pernicious anaemia; he may have determined those conditions of life, climatic and otherwise, under which the organism with its special liabilities may work efficiently and show no overt weakness. In psychiatry the same general principles are also involved, but the missing elements may be social factors over which the psychiatrist has little control; spiritual or social vitamins are not easily supplied, it is not easy to find the mental climate which will allow a placid existence and not elicit an underlying instability or defect.

The trends of investigation and interpretation which we have discussed have respectively emphasized impersonal factors (the various physiological mechanisms and external noxae), personal factors (the structure of the personality with its special lines of sensitiveness), environmental factors (the family, social atmosphere, gen-

eral culture). In each of these fields increase of
knowledge has raised important questions with
regard to treatment and to prevention. In each of
these fields important gains have been made and
indications for a program of amelioration outlined. One can refer to such obvious gains as the
improvement in the treatment of general paralysis,
a diagnosis which at the beginning of the century
meant a sentence to death within two to five years,
while now one expects one-third of the patients
admitted to hospitals with this diagnosis to be
restored to occupational efficiency, and another
third to maintain a modest degree of social
adaptation for a prolonged period. In regard to
the second field, where difficulties within the personality are important, one may refer to the much
more precise and far-reaching treatment of the
psychoneuroses and of many cases of distorted and
inhibited personality. As to the environmental
factors, one may point to cases where the appreciation of this factor with resultant modification of
the atmosphere in the home, the schoolroom, or
the factory, or with transfer to a different environment, has brought about quite dramatic
changes.

Quite apart from the more immediate and
striking results of the various modes of attack,

each of the latter has both contributed insight into the mechanisms of the disorders and suggested a further investigative and therapeutic program of continued endeavor. There is at the present moment a note of hopefulness in the air and much earnestness and enthusiasm, even with full realization of the complexity of the task.

We do not know to what extent and in exactly what cases benefit may be derived from drug treatment, from endocrinologic treatment, from physiotherapy and the various procedures of internal medicine.

The extent to which the individual case of mental disorder can be modified by a painstaking and prolonged review of the internal equilibrium of the personality is difficult to determine. Conventional diagnostic terms with their traditional emphasis on statistical prognosis frequently discourage therapeutic effort. How often is a painstaking attempt made to deal in a thorough way with a manic-depressive attack, so apt to be dismissed as a self-limiting process? With a case of dementia praecox of which the prognosis is supposed to be given by the name? With a case of paranoia, the fixity of whose ideas is an established dogma? One has only begun to deal with these conditions as problems of human adaptation, and time will show how far and under what conditions it may be possible to help many patients, who now are considered more as problems in management than as problems for fundamental treatment.

With regard to the influence of the environment on the individual case it is now recognized that many symptoms, previously attributed to a hypothetical underlying process, are to a large extent the result of the unwholesome conditions enforced by the withdrawal of the patient from the normal conditions of community life, and by the economic limitations of the hospital which preclude it from supplying the individual patient with the conditions necessary for the maintenance of interest and for the utilization of his actual assets. The striking results sometimes attained by the transfer of a patient from a familiar institutional environment to a new scene, and by the energetic and consistent development of occupational therapy, furnish lessons which are far from having been thoroughly assimilated.

One should avoid giving the impression that treatment is exclusively limited in the individual case to one or another of the three main fields of endeavor. In the individual case it may be necessary to treat the physical health, the metabolism, the focal infection, as well as to deal with the internal equilibrium of the patient, and to see whether the patient can be relieved of undue environmental strains or receive some more support from the social group. Psychiatry deals with the individual as a whole, and should furnish help at whatever level it may be available. The enthusiast may concentrate exclusively on one avenue of approach and on one line of treatment, but the trend of psychiatric thought is to emphasize the integration of all the component forces, which may have to be discussed separately but which are only abstract aspects of the unitary organism. As the functions of that organism may be disturbed at various levels and from various directions, so in the restoration or amelioration of function psychiatry recognizes that it must be willing to utilize all the resources that are at its disposal.

II

THE STUFF OF LIFE
AND THE SCHIZO-
PHRENIC REACTION

IN the first lecture a very summary review was given of the various fields cultivated in the investigation of the causes and treatment of mental disorders. Some investigators into the nature of mental disorders have intensively followed clues to the possible deficiency of one or another of the bodily systems or to the presence of external noxae. Others have concentrated on qualities of the personality which could not be resolved into simpler physiological elements, and which in conjunction with the specific life situation seemed to determine that special portion of the life history of the individual called *the psychosis*.

Both lines of investigation produced an important body of facts, valuable not only for the interpretation but also for the treatment of mental disorders. There was a natural tendency for workers who had concentrated on one aspect of

the situation to overvalue their methods and results, and to present too exclusive formulations.
Thus there seemed to be contradiction and opposition between those working at the problem with the
methods of the basal medical sciences and those
who were studying the dynamics of the personality
at the psychological level. The data of the various
groups are, however, not in opposition to but
rather supplement each other, and an adequate
formulation of mental disorders has to do justice
to all the facts gathered from diverse sources.

In this lecture I propose to come a little closer
to the actual stuff of psychiatry, and to discuss
some of the problems which meet us in individual
cases. The material has been observed in the
service of a busy psychopathic hospital where the
work is largely determined by conditions of practical service and not merely by considerations of
scientific procedure. The approach to the individual case is catholic, and the effort is made to
apportion their respective values to somatic, personal, and environmental factors, and to step in
therapeutically wherever there is a chance of being
of help. As to the program of research, some investigations have dealt with the fundamental
bodily processes, other investigations have focused
upon the contribution made by the personality

itself to the development of the psychosis, especially the more serious type of psychosis. It is this latter material which I now propose to discuss.

The intimate relation between personality and mental disorder is most generally recognized in relation to the special group of mental disorders or psychoses which we call psychoneuroses, i.e. in relation to hysteria, morbid fears, compulsive conditions. In these conditions it is generally conceded that the clinical picture is adequately resolved into its components when one demonstrates the sequence of events in terms of personal experience and of objective situation. It is true that, while this personality analysis of the individual case is a satisfactory formulation for practical purposes, there are still interesting theoretical problems as to the exact determination of the special symptoms at the somatic level by physiological idiosyncrasies or acquired weaknesses, either permanent or transitory.

In other psychoses, too, we are accustomed to lay the main emphasis on a special quality of the personality, although a quality very different from that characteristic of the psychoneuroses. Thus in the affective or manic-depressive psychoses, the fundamental basis of which is so obscure, we look upon the affective vulnerability of the patient as a quality of the organism, which we can at present neither resolve into simpler psychological nor physiological components.

In regard to the great group of mental disorders which remain after we put aside the above, and the organic, the toxic, and the symptomatic psychoses, how far does the study of the personality and of the life situation render the individual case intelligible and offer a guide with regard to treatment and prevention? Is it worth while to study intensively the personality of these patients and the life situation, or is the clue to the essential nature of these disorders to be found by histopathological, biochemical, physiological or bacteriological methods? We can at least say that so far these latter methods have not given us any convincing or complete interpretation of these disorders; we have no guarantee that the solution of the problems must necessarily be found by these methods. It seems, therefore, quite reasonable to retain our interest in the personality of the patient and in his specific life situation and to consider whether they too may not throw some light on the disorder.

The review of personal traits and of the details of experience may shock those who seek for explanation only in the depths of the organic processes. Interest in the detailed life histories of patients and explanations based on such material may seem to smack of "the psychology of the janitor." The janitor, however, may observe what escapes the professor; the former, observing human nature in its undress appearance, may be able to make important observations on human weaknesses which are not revealed on parade.

The group of cases which have occupied us may seem to require positive definition and delimitation; so far we have indicated it in a rather broad way by exclusion. The delimitation is a matter of considerable difficulty in view of the fact that we are dealing with life histories of the greatest diversity, with clinical pictures which contain no fixed and dependable pathognomic sign, no Argyll Robertson pupil nor sign of Babinski, no Widal nor Wassermann reaction, no established histopathology. Experience teaches us that on the whole the clinical pictures presented by these cases are of serious outcome. On the other hand recovery is not unknown, and the factors upon which the course of the disorder depends are difficult to demonstrate.

I shall not try to define the exact characteristics of the patients in this group nor specify the numerous variations in the clinical picture. We are not concerned with detailed symptomatology but with general principles. One may note as an outstanding characteristic that these patients are more seriously estranged from their normal fellows than the patients in the other groups which we have mentioned; they are more alien to us, their emotional life, their motivation, their outlook on the world have a certain bizarre and unintelligible quality. It is to a certain extent this unintelligible quality as well as the serious degree to which the patient may be crippled that makes the assumption of some underlying disease so plausible.

I use the standard terms with the greatest of hesitation, but I must admit that the problem I am discussing is to a large extent the same as the problem of dementia praecox. Instead of considering patients with the diagnosis dementia praecox as having a "disease," I prefer to think of them as belonging to a Greek letter society, the conditions for admission to which are obscure; inclusion in and exclusion from the fraternity are determined by considerations which may vary from year to year and from place to place, and the directing board is not known.

Kraepelin, to whom we owe the dominance of the concept of dementia praecox, considered that the later phases of a mental disorder give the truest insight into its nature and make its interpretation and its classification more certain. He therefore selected the more serious cases of this group which we are about to discuss, those who seemed to be permanently crippled mentally, and on the basis of this clinical material with the deterioration so frequently observed he developed, although with some qualifications, the concept of a unitary disorder. He assumed that the observed disorder was the expression of some underlying disease or diseases, and that the psychological symptoms were merely the disturbances caused by the underlying impersonal process. The investigation of this process would naturally utilize the ordinary methods employed in the investigation of disease processes.

As to the forms which this disease might take, his earlier grouping was into three main forms; the hebephrenic, the catatonic, and the paranoid. He later felt that this classification failed to do justice to the variety of clinical pictures, and he industriously tried to separate into more homogeneous groups the large collection of patients to whom he had attached the name dementia praecox. Bleuler, profoundly influenced by the doctrines of Freud, showed the personal significance of many of the symptoms of dementia praecox, and ex-

panded the Kraepelinian group into the less rigid
group of the schizophrenias. Between the normal
and the schizophrenic individual he considered
that there still yawned a gap which the discovery
of a disease process alone would enable the physician to bridge.

The Kraepelinian formulation seems to draw
rather definite boundaries where no actual boundaries exist; it gives an appearance of certainty with
regard to prognosis which the facts hardly war-
rant; the personality receives scant attention; the
life situation is considered to be more or less irrelevant. There seems to be no sound reason for
basing the interpretation of a group of cases on
the study of the more severe cases and of the
later stages, unless these cases and these stages
demonstrate the presence of some definite factors
of unequivocal nature which in retrospect throw
light on the early stages of the disorder. As a
matter of fact, the exact significance of the deterioration in the severe cases is still uncertain.
The actual degree and nature of this deterioration are not necessarily the expression of some
specific factor which gives the key to the whole
disorder, but may be due to a great variety
of internal and external factors. The essential
principles of the disorder in those cases which

end in bankruptcy may be the same as in other cases in which, however, there are enough assets, internal or external, to make recovery possible.

In the present discussion we are concerned with a group of patients, which we leave poorly delimited and vaguely characterized, consisting of individuals who are failures from the point of view of the social group, failures of a special type, failures temporary or permanent. We shall discuss them with no preconception as to the presence of any disease, but shall consider them as troubled souls or non-conformists who happen to be available for study. Even a modern community finds non-conformity disturbing and unpleasant, but with softened manners takes the non-conformist to a psychopathic hospital instead of subjecting him to mediaeval or primitive penalties. The fact that an individual is sojourning in a psychopathic hospital is not presumptive evidence of disease. It indicates that he feels in need of help, on account of some inner handicap or disharmony, or that his fellows find him a perplexing or disturbing member of the group. The difficulty may be the result of an underlying disease or it may be a maladaptation of more complicated origin. To understand the nature of the disharmony or maladaptation one must take into consideration not only the facts of internal medicine but also the complex forces involved in the human personality and the environmental factors involved in a single life history. With so many variables each clinical picture is bound to have its individual stamp, each patient is mentally disordered in his own individual way. The orderly classification of material is thus a matter of great difficulty, and it is not easy to present the results of extensive observation and analysis in any brief systematic body of doctrine.

The idea that every patient is an individual problem and not merely a particular example of a recognized disorder is to some disturbing. Order is heaven's first law, and the craving for order and system has dominated the formulations of many psychiatrists. Some have a horror of a case being left unclassified, even though its individual structure be understood and the program of treatment definite; the record must not be left more or less in the air, but should fit into the prevailing order of a psychiatric system. Some workers have even believed in maintaining a certain orderly balance between the various groups of cases. I can remember the chairman of a staff conference uttering a mild protest at a diagnosis of dementia praecox, "the dementia praecox group is getting rather large, doctor." I can also remember a physician justifying the presentation of a case not quite in accord with the facts as being due to his desire to make it a correct and orderly sample of the condition diagnosed (dementia praecox). Life, however, is not a very orderly process; unexpected, irregular, unusual situations develop. Human nature is a very imperfect system, the individual is not a standardized article. No rigid system of classification can do justice to the great variety of life experience.

On the other hand, however chaotic life may be, however varied human nature, in surveying the experiences of our patients one is repeatedly confronted by the same reactions, the same major forces and major issues. We see a certain limitation in the number of ways in which man meets the challenge of the environment, and we can outline certain general principles regarding the disorders observed. If we are going to make any headway in the analysis of our problems, and if the experimental method is not available, we have to group together cases which have a certain degree of similarity, and by studying these groups separate what is individual and incidental from what is general and essential.

In surveying our schizophrenic material an endeavor was made to form more or less homogeneous groups, not for mere description and classification, but as a first step toward a dynamic analysis of the cases, with special attention paid to the personal and environmental factors. A provisional survey of this material has been made but the details of even 150 lives are somewhat overwhelming. I do not propose to submit any statistical data but to discuss some of the impressions derived from the survey. In this discussion, although the terms of Kraepelin are little used, and little reference is made to formal symptomatology, it will be obvious that the groups described correspond in a general way to the hebephrenic, catatonic, paranoid forms of dementia praecox.

It will be obvious that the groups here described are far from being homogeneous, but even this first classification may serve as a basis for discussion and help to clarify our thought about certain aspects of this material. To focus attention temporarily on these aspects does not mean to undervalue the importance of the impersonal factors, of the data of pathological anatomy and physiology. The following discussion is a partial, not a comprehensive, presentation of the subject. With this understanding we proceed to some comments upon our provisional groups.

Group I

Patients presenting a clinical picture of non-adaptive turmoil or disturbance of function

The first group of cases into which our material naturally falls is characterized by the fact that the symptoms seem to be without any special adaptive significance and are not integrated into any very definite pattern. The symptoms are more or less fragmentary. In the different patients there are variable and unstable emotional reactions of diverse type.

In general, one may say that the clinical picture shows a non-adaptive disturbance of function; there is emotional turmoil, disturbance of behavior and of the thought processes, and in the disturbance of behavior a frequent symptom is the crude or disguised expression of previously repressed pleasure-seeking tendencies. While many of the individual symptoms seem to indicate a mere non-adaptive disturbance of function and the general picture is that of a condition of disharmony and turmoil, the disturbance as a whole may in some cases have an adaptive significance. Thus the total clinical picture may in some cases be a disguised declaration of irresponsibility, of wayward self-assertion, of abandonment to emotional reactions and to impulses. It may have the adaptive significance of a rejection of adult responsibility and of an appeal for childhood immunities and privileges. It may have the significance of a prison psychosis or of the *Faxensyndrom* of Bleuler. In the majority of cases one sees no clear evidence of such an adaptive rôle; the symptoms represent mere disorder, the inability of the personality to maintain its equilibrium, whether this inability be due to a latent morbid process, to inner tension of complex nature, or to external stress.

In the clinical picture one emphasizes the shallowness or the incongruity of the emotional reactions, the impulsive or erratic motivation, the affected or strained utterances, attitudes and movements, the presence of hallucinations. In some cases the emotional reaction is less incongruous; there may be marked fear, perplexity, anger, suspicion. The number of cases which present a silly appearance with shallow affective reaction is small in comparison with those which present a jumbled picture of disturbed emotion, fragmentary delusions, erratic behavior.

In each case one attempts to find the source of the individual symptoms and of any fragmentary patterns of reaction. A mood of perplexity or of fear may be connected with inner conflicts; these inner conflicts frequently involve the sex appetite, pleasure-seeking tendencies, the bond of affection between child and parent. The misinterpretation of the environment is frequently intelligible in the light of repressed factors. The sources of the impulsive and wayward conduct can frequently be traced. The occurrence of the psychosis serves as a measure of the robustness of the individual's personality, the degree of mental tension, the severity of the particular life problems. The prognosis has to be given in the light of such a review. A breakdown under little provocation shows a vulnerable or unstable personality. A more robust personality may break down under circumstances of exceptional difficulty. The breakdown may show that beneath an apparently stable equilibrium there had been a condition of very great tension. In some cases the breakdown is only the last stage of a long period of unsatisfactory adaptation, in others the psychosis is a startling interruption of what appeared to be a fairly well-adjusted life. In some cases the patient appears to be in excellent physical health, in others one finds a variety of bodily ailments. In some cases there is fairly rapid recovery, in other cases the outcome may be permanent impairment of the personality to an extreme degree.

The discussion of the issues involved in this clinical material tends to become general and elusive, unless one considers particular instances and stirs in some concrete facts as William James would stir in a few ideas to give substance to a discussion which threatened to become rather thin.

Anna B., a young woman of eighteen, devoted to her invalid mother, shy, seclusive, uncommunicative, excessively clean and proper, was insistent on getting her own way (she had temper tantrums in childhood). At the age of eighteen she accepted a formal proposal of marriage which she had been afraid might not be forthcoming. One week after her engagement she complained of headache, vague general pains, exhaustion. The same evening she was much frightened by a trifling incident, the failure to recognize a friend of the family as he entered the dark hall. She was petrified and repeated "he has got me in a trap." The same night she was excited, called for her mother, talked incoherently. She said she had been assaulted by this man and that the whole world was jealous, that people were accusing her of sexual misconduct, making fun of her engagement. In a general hospital her physical condition was considered as presenting nothing of note. During the following days she wanted to die, refused to eat, had to be fed by tube. She made sudden rushes to the window. She refused to go to the toilet. She continued for over two months to present considerable difficulty in management and was then admitted for a few days to the Boston Psychopathic Hospital. She was in a state of emotional excitement, she sobbed, screamed, and resisted the care of the nurses. She soiled and wet herself. Her talk was vague and disjointed. She was much dehydrated, had persistent diarrhoea, temperature 99.8°F. (rectal) on admission. One blood count was 19,300 w.b.c.; report from a previous examination stated that the hematological studies were negative.

During the total course of the mental disorder the patient had referred to various topics. At the beginning she had complained of being assaulted, thought that people were criticizing her sexual conduct. She said, "If I eat it will kill my brother." Somewhat later she said, "I am a scandal and I am killing others, they are suffering pain for me"; "I want to be punished for my sins, to die in case I kill them all." After a few days in the Boston Psycopathic Hospital the patient was taken home. When seen at home a few months later she seemed perfectly well, more carefree and less sensitive than she had ever been before. One year later she was still in good health and preparing for her wedding.

In this somewhat fragmentary observation we have a benign psychosis in which some physical symptoms are present—malaise, headache and vague complaints at the beginning, some diarrhoea later, one high white blood count—but no well-defined somatic disorder of recognized course. One has to consider, however, the possibility that some fundamental somatic ailment not only explains these symptoms, but is also the cause of the disturbance of the complex functions. An intoxication of unknown origin might explain the mental confusion, the incoherence, the fear, the scattered hallucinations, the inattention to cleanliness. On the other hand, throughout the whole sickness the feeling of guilt seems rather prominent. She wishes to kill herself, she is a scandal, a source of danger and contamination to others.

In reviewing the clinical picture one notes both the disturbance of the sensorium which we are accustomed to associate with impersonal processes, as well as with conditions of emotional stress, and at the same time the fact that her behavior and her utterances bear the stamp of special preoccupation with her personal value and her relation to the group. There come to the surface, perhaps as a release phenomenon, ideas of guilt, unworthiness, atonement, danger to others (primitive thought). It appears, therefore, that the complex forces of the personality play a certain rôle in determining the clinical picture. Whether weakened by a somatic disorder or by emotional disturbance the patient deals with the world in a distorted way, and the mode of the distortion is determined by her internal conflicts.

The second case is that of a young man of twenty-five (Bernard C.) who three weeks after a radical operation on the maxillary sinuses complained of being nervous and began to say nonsensical things, of which no details were available. On admission to the hospital he was mildly confused, but knew that he was in a mental hospital, gave the day of the month and the month correctly, but the year as 1928 (May, 1929). He seemed somewhat puzzled, was slow in his movements, did not always carry out simple demands. He showed both echopraxia and echolalia. He felt that the other patients talked about him and that his family had discarded him. He was afraid that his family would be murdered. The pharynx and tongue were a beefy red; post-nasal discharge;

pulse 96, temperature 100°F., w.b.c. 21,700; neurological status negative. After the first week in the hospital the patient showed no fever; the surgeon saw no reason for any further interference with the sinuses. During the following three months in hospital the patient was somewhat restless and agitated, and at times tearful. He would hear his mother's voice; he thought that his family was going to be killed; he often sat with a preoccupied air; he harped on the topic of going home. He was as a rule oriented. His general physical condition was satisfactory and owing to his eagerness to go home he was discharged, although he was still slow and preoccupied. As he did not improve at home he had to be admitted to a state hospital where he talked very little and was practically unintelligible. He was tense and at times restless, with grimacing and facial twitching; he was also at times noted as fairly cheerful, childish, uneasy. He soiled and wet himself; he had occasionally to be tube-fed. He was very difficult to care for owing to his aggressive behavior. Death on December 20, 1931, was attributed to broncho-pneumonia and chronic myocarditis; no autopsy.

To summarize: on the basis of a chronic sinusitis with acute exacerbation and surgical operation the patient develops a general difficulty of mental operations, a mood of some distress with a few depressive ideas; behavior is seriously modified, there is echolalia and echopraxia, rather aimless antagonistic behavior, harping on the desire to return home. In this case we see little contribution from special tendencies in the personality in contrast with the preceding case, the fiancée of nineteen. There is little in the symptomatology that is adaptive. The picture is that of a mere disturbance of complex functions, possibly of infective origin.

The third case is that of a factory worker of twenty (Charles D.), devoted to his mother, who began to be rather uproarious and boastful in his factory, so that he had to be taken to the hospital. There he talked freely of his personal experiences, said that he got pleasing magnetic feelings from various sources; he thought that at church the holy images were alive, claimed that God was in communication with him and that he saw God. He elaborated many curious statements about cosmic forces, their erotic effect, his communications with God. Although elated and talkative and rambling, he showed no rhyming. The clinical picture seemed benign, and the patient had been normally sociable without any special anomaly of character. He was discharged to his family after nine days, and a few days later was able to resume his education in the high school. A few months later he was well and doing quite responsible work. The sister of this patient in a state hospital is considered to be a case of dementia praecox, catatonic form.

The fourth case is that of a high-school boy of sixteen (David E.), brought up in a home of discord with a domineering father. The patient had felt for some time that his family was against him and that he was unwanted. He was rather odd in his behavior; a fair student. He was ordered from home after an altercation, and went to stay with a relative. There he was described as very filthy; he did not sleep for four nights and paced the floor; he was frightened. When taken home he remained listless, ate little, felt that his mother had poisoned his food; he said and did queer things; he flashed a huge flashlight on his sister while she was bathing her baby. He was rather obstinate and when driven to some relatives he refused to leave the auto and insisted on driving all night. In the hospital he was rather depressed and frequently failed to reply to questions. He talked of being followed by a big man; he was evidently afraid. On leaving the hospital after a stay of six days he did poorly at school but fairly well on a farm. On his return home there was again an altercation, which led to his admission to a state hospital.

In this case one has a difficult boy brought up in a home of discord, who under rather trying circumstances shows a disturbance of mood, fear, somewhat erratic conduct, and makes accusations such as that his mother is poisoning his food; nothing indicates the importance of any somatic factor, and the condition seems to be the reaction of an unstable personality to a difficult situation.

The fifth patient, a teacher, twenty-four years of age (Frieda G.), was somewhat depressed by her work, felt herself a failure, tried to commit suicide. When restrained by the police and given a sedative by a physician she thought that her sisters had wanted to compromise her sexually with the police, that the physician had given her poison to kill her, that everybody was against her. She passed through various phases of distressed over-activity and of silent under-activity. In the hospital she talked of vague sinister happenings, appeared suspicious of poison, talked in a religious strain. When transferred to a state hospital she was mute, untidy, grimaced, gesticulated, and for some time she was dirty, unresponsive and vacant in appearance. One month after this she began to improve rapidly, and two months later was able to go home, but made a poor adjustment and was readmitted to the hospital; there she was very difficult to manage and would attack the nurses. After a few months the patient seemed to make a good recovery, left the hospital again, and within the year she married.

The question may arise whether these cases are relevant to our present problem, whether they have any close kinship to the main group of cases we are discussing or whether there is only a superficial resemblance. The young girl of nineteen, upset after her engagement, with her marked mental confusion and some indications of a somatic ailment, might be looked upon as having some physical disorder with incidental mental symptoms. Still more so the young man with the sinusitis, the apparently meaningless disturbance of behavior, the fatal termination. The third case with his boastfulness, productivity and free activity might be looked upon as having a special affective instability and the material that came up with its erotic and religious coloring might be considered to be merely incidental. The fourth case might be

looked upon as a very unstable boy who, in a difficult situation, behaves in an emotional, impulsive
and erratic way and makes uncritical accusations.
The fifth case might more generally be accepted
as belonging to our special group.

Let us admit that our first provisional grouping
has been superficial; let us eliminate the young
fiancée with her vague complaints, the man with
the sinusitis, the lad with the affective disorder, the
other lad with his explosive personality. There remains a considerable number of other cases in
whom there is no adequate evidence of somatic
disorder, no indication of a specific type of vulnerability such as the affective constitution, and yet in
whom we find a clinical picture not dissimilar from
that of the above cases, and apparently composed
of the same elements.

The following additional cases chosen more or
less at random may serve as suitable material to
illustrate the group of patients under discussion.

A lad of seventeen (Edgar F.), the mother a
general paralytic, the father a dissolute man, had
lived under sordid conditions, been ill-treated by
the housekeeper. He told his father of worry over
autoerotism; he became very seclusive, would not
see his friends, looked out of the window sus-

piciously. He said that his stomach was lined with acid. He had a washing ritual. He did extremely crude things, urinated on the floor, came into a room naked. He made suicidal attempts. In the hospital he was restless and extremely crude in his behavior, continued to soil and wet the floor. He said that poison had been put in his food. He thrust his hand through a window. He was distractible, had flight of ideas, frequently would sing and whistle. In this case in face of internal and external difficulties there is abandonment of adaptation to social demands and surrender to crude tendencies. The physical status was not noteworthy; Wassermann reaction of blood and cerebrospinal fluid negative.

A clerk (George H.), twenty-three years of age, had shown the normal interests of a young man, was in good physical health. One morning he perplexed his brother by asking an odd question; the same day he returned home with his face disfigured after some altercation. For a few days he seemed dazed and blank. He then told his sister to say an act of contrition, and talked incoherently. He thought that the world was changed, warned his brother "to eat very little," wondered if his own mind were going. In the hospital he was very erratic in his conduct and utterances; he told of autoerotism, perverse sexual activity, ruminations over guilt and atonement. After a few days of erratic and impulsive behavior he became stuporous. After two years the patient was still in a mental hospital, was described as silly and apathetic.

A bookkeeper of twenty-seven (Isabel K.), an only child, daughter of a syphilitic father, had been efficient in her work and socially well-balanced. She began to be worried, irritable and sensitive about the influence of a fellow worker on her; she lost sleep and appetite. After remaining several months at home she suddenly developed a condition of emotional tension, complained of pain or pressure in the head, said she was insane, referred to "Holy Father," attempted to go undressed on the street. In the hospital she talked little and in a fragmentary way about trivial incidents, about her affection for her father, visions of God, voices, internal conflicts. She showed erotic behavior, misinterpreted the nurses' behavior as erotic, wet and soiled herself. She wrote childish letters; in general her condition was one of emotional shallowness and indifference. During the following year she lived at home a life of rigidly stereotyped routine with little activity and no interest in her personal appearance or cleanliness. On later read-mission to hospital she spoke at times in a precise and stilted way; people could read her mind, God had talked to her since girlhood. Physical examination throughout the course of her illness failed to throw light on the condition; the blood Wasser-mann was negative.

A woman of twenty-nine (Katharine L.), de-voted to the religious life, a rather submissive and inefficient person, from girlhood onwards had con-flicts over autoerotism and homosexual tendencies. In the setting of the religious life she developed a nervous condition, expressed first undue devotion and then antagonism to a superior, became con-fused, showed erratic behavior. In the hospital she misidentified the woman physician in a religious sense, was erratic and impulsive, showed crude homosexual activity, demanded a knife to cut out her bowels, talked of voices and visions. Her physical health was good.

During the following year she continued to show crude, erratic and aggressive conduct, re-ferred to voices of religious origin, talked to her-self incoherently.

A schoolboy of seventeen (Lawrence M.), am-bitious, somewhat estranged from his ignorant

family, preoccupied with his brother's insanity, became sensitive and seclusive, felt that he had
special hypnotic power, had hallucinations of
elusive nature accompanied by partial insight
("but it is in my mind—it's exactly like a noise");
he was picked up by the police late at night wan-
dering about the streets. He wondered if he were
a radio, a broadcasting station, a mind reader, a
hypnotist. He was afraid he or his mother might
be killed; people talked about it when they looked
at him. He had a slight transitory fever
(T. 101.2°) with no other somatic symptoms.
This condition of acute turmoil was succeeded by
a stuporous period of three months, and then by
a period of over-activity and attitudinizing, and
during the following two years the patient spent
much of his time in a mental hospital.

A colored woman of twenty-nine (Martha N.),
deserted by her husband, felt her loneliness after
she had to send away her only son to relatives. A
spiritualistic suitor had replaced the husband.
Ruminating over the unsatisfactory marital situation she was depressed, finally became confused
and excited, claimed she was in communication
with God; somewhat later she expressed a fear
that someone might kill her, that she might kill

herself, that her husband was influencing her in an occult way. She became semi-stuporous, asked whether she were alive or dead; had visual and auditory hallucinations. After two years in a mental hospital, during which there had been periods of excitement and periods of stupor, her behavior was rather dilapidated, she was erratic and violent, untidy, aggressive.

A clerk (Norman O.), twenty-five years of age, who had been brought up by a nervous mother, deserted by her alcoholic husband, for one year had been preoccupied about his health without objective ground. One day he perplexed his brother with curious remarks, and on the following days complained of exhaustion, talked in an incoherent way as if intoxicated, was sleepless and afraid; voices said to him "you have it," God was inside him. In the hospital the patient showed queer theatrical behavior, talked with little evidence of emotion in a fragmentary way about being killed, about having been poisoned, about being God. Voices spoke to him, but no significant content was elicited. The patient was clearly oriented, apparently had good memory. After some months the patient made a very good impression and tried to resume life in the community, but was unsuccessful. On his return to the hospital, although the surface behavior was good, he was seclusive, smiled in an unexplained manner, constantly heard voices.

In face of the challenge of such patients as those cited above there are various alternatives open to us. We may leave the clinical picture of the individual case as a familiar descriptive unit, and admit our complete ignorance of its underlying nature. We may look upon the clinical picture as symptomatic of an underlying disease, and make an intensive search for the disease. A third possibility is to take the clinical picture as one phase of the life of an individual and try to understand that phase. A case seen once for a few minutes during a hospital visit may serve to illustrate the point under discussion. The patient was a young lad sitting in the ward with relaxed posture, his clothes somewhat stained and soiled from his poor table manners, in his hand a crust of bread firmly clasped. The general clinical picture was familiar. From the point of view of social adaptation his behavior was inferior; the inferior conduct might be attributed to some subtle underlying morbid process. A brief interview elicited a few utterances. The lad referred to the crust of bread in his hand as *the staff of life;* he told of preoccupation with his past sex behavior and with judgments of moral value. Preoccupied with thoughts of his spiritual welfare he was clinging strenuously to the hope of salvation symbolized by the crust of bread which he held in his hand. Beneath the clinical picture of dilapidated conduct was a human drama. In that drama the patient was groping for a solution of his difficulties. He had found only a second-rate symbolic solution which did not enable him to resume his normal rôle as a worker among his fellows; it was at least an attempt at a solution, it indicated to the physician the presence of a conflict of a very familiar and serious type.

It may be well, therefore, in each individual case, even of apparently meaningless disorder, to consider it as a fragment of a life history, as a drama, as a period of conflict, a conflict of which the solution may be difficult and the outcome very dubious. As to the nature of the conflict, as one goes over a series of cases one meets the same topics again and again; they are the fundamental issues of human life. We meet the insistent urge of the appetites, especially the sexual appetite and all its components. We meet the strong desire to be of value and to have prestige and to escape from a feeling of guilt or of inferiority. We meet the craving for a sound bond of affection between oneself and the family and one's fellows.

Such is the content of the drama, and in this first group of cases which we are discussing its elements are woven into no coherent plot, no solution is in sight. In some patients the rupture of the previous equilibrium has been final, little effort is shown toward integration at a better level, there is surrender, acceptance of defeat, disintegration, deterioration. In other cases there may be a return to the previous equilibrium, the internal situation may not have been so devastating and the conflict not so unequal, the assets of the personality more rich, the situation more favorable. In other cases there is not a return to a wholesome social integration; there are assets enough, however, to weave some sort of coherent pattern out of the fragments of the drama, there is a certain integration into the structure of a tolerant social group. The patient has found, to a certain extent, a solution of his conflict, but at the price of a surrender of his social rôle in the real world.

With this point of view, when we look back on the first four cases at first provisionally included, then provisionally discarded, do we see any kinship with the present group? In their case is there any human drama to be discussed, or is the drama

one at the impersonal level where organisms deal
with the defences of the tissues and the tissues try
to acquire the matter and energy needed for their
efficient working?

In the case of the young fiancée one may perhaps
assume an underlying somatic disorder, but during
the months of her sickness the patient was preoccupied with the feeling of her moral worth, with
the problem of guilt, of contamination, of her
reputation. She felt that she might as well do away
with herself, she felt that her behavior was of in-
finite importance to the human race. Here, too,
we see the same drama as in our other patients
with unimpaired physical health, only it is the
drama of a heroine perhaps somewhat handi-
capped by some obscure physical ailment. It seems
justifiable in the study of such a case to do justice
to the drama while not neglecting the physical ailment. In the drama with the hero crippled by
sinusitis, his handicap may make any elaborate plot
impossible, his movements are not altogether the
significant movements of the actor but partly those
of the sick man, his slowness and his stickiness
may be the expression of organic incapacity rather
than the indication of discouragement or appeal
or surrender. Yet, notwithstanding the seriousness
of the organic impairment, we see indications of

the same personal conflicts as in our other cases. He feels that everyone is talking about him, he believes the family want to get rid of him, he clamors to get home to the mother who spoiled him; he is afraid that his family will be murdered, he talks about making the sign of the cross (he is a Jew); he reproaches himself with a serious sexual misdemeanor in the distant past; he feels that he has been mocking people in the hospital.

In the case of the exalted young man of twenty who made such a quick recovery, the drama which he plays in his condition of mild exhilaration and lack of inhibition is rather simple; he vibrates to the harmony of the spheres and the whole of existence has a pleasing erotic quality, he has a philosophy of life to communicate to the world.

In the difficult boy of sixteen we see great emotional tension in relation to the difficult family situation, and fragmentary behavior, the significance of which escapes us; there is the neglect of ordinary personal care, aimless and restless behavior, accusations of being poisoned, perhaps mere provocative expressions of anger rather than indications of a distorted belief. It is the peculiar behavior of the boy in this setting of emotional turmoil that suggests and perhaps justifies the provisional grouping of the patient with the other cases.

This further review of our first four cases may justify us in retaining them within our first group, while we realize that this kinship does not exhaust their complexity.

In these cases of turmoil which form our first group we see essentially a break in compensation, a marked disturbance of the normal integrated activity. With the break in compensation repressed factors assert themselves; the break itself may be due to the fact that the tension associated with these repressed factors has become too great for the capacity of the individual. In the light of such episodes we estimate the degree of repression which different individuals can stand, the time during which they can repress forbidden desires and feelings of guilt or hate, and chain up seductive phantasies. The psychosis is a valuable revelation of the personality; in the psychosis as in wine the truth appears.

In discussing the course of the disorder in this first group of patients reference has been made to the fact that in some cases which begin with such a period of unadaptive disturbance or turmoil the patient may not go on to profound deterioration, nor on the other hand make a satisfactory recovery, but may establish an equilibrium of inferior type perhaps only temporary. Thus the patient at a later stage of his disorder may be found included in our second group of cases, where the central symptom is withdrawal of interest from the outside world, or in the third group, the striking feature of which is the subjective reconstruction of the world picture in response to the inner needs of the individual.

Group II

Patients presenting lack of interest in or response to the external world

In the second group of patients with their withdrawal of interest from or their lessened response to the outside world, we have again the alternative of regarding the behavior and outlook of the patient as a manifestation of some impersonal disease process or as an inferior or ineffective individual response to the challenge of the life situation. The fact that this group includes many patients with fixed postures, odd gestures and movements, catalepsy, waxy flexibility, symptoms somewhat similar to those observed in encephalitic patients and in bulbocapninized cats, has favored the impersonal interpretation of these disorders, an interpretation rendered the more plausible in some cases by the disappearance of the special symptoms, at least temporarily, under the influence of drugs.

Leaving aside for the present the interpretation of the motor symptoms, one may discuss the general symptomatology and course of the disorder in this group of patients. As to the course, the disorder may end in permanent impairment of the personality, or on the other hand may be followed by complete restoration to previous efficiency. It is not to be assumed that the difference of outcome necessarily indicates a difference in the nature of the underlying disorder. An unfavorable outcome may be due to a constellation of unfavorable external factors, and to an absence of those personal assets or recuperative powers which in the favorable cases allow a restoration to the previous level, as in the benign stupors studied by Hoch. So hysteria may be a transitory manifestation or a prolonged and crippling disorder, depending on the original endowment of the individual, his past experience and actual life situation.

The study of the significance of the symptoms in this second group of cases is a matter of great practical difficulty. The coöperation of a certain number of psychoneurotic patients enables one to make an analysis of psychoneurotic mechanisms, which is valid even for those cases where analysis may not be possible. In those mental disorders in which the patient withdraws his interest from the outside world the lack of contact of the patient with the physician, sometimes accompanied by antagonism to or aggression towards the physician, makes the analysis of the individual case largely a matter of conjecture, and the factors which determine the evolution of the clinical picture and its outcome remain obscure. Even the recovered patient may give little coöperation in a thorough study of the whole psychosis. In many cases after recovery from a stupor it is impossible to obtain from the patient any data which throw light upon the condition. The patient may claim to have forgotten the content of his experience during the stupor, even though he may retain memory of the objective happenings of the same period.

In some patients diminished interest in the environment is almost the whole problem. In other cases an apathetic or stuporous period is merely one phase in a complex psychosis in which other patterns of reaction occur. The lack of response to the values in the environment may be only partial. There may be a lack of external response, but even in severe cases where the overt behavior of the individual indicates no response, the use of the psychogalvanometer, or other technique, may demonstrate a very definite autonomic response to environmental stimuli. While in some cases there may be an active withdrawal of interest from and even a positive rejection of the environment, in other cases there seems to be a mere lack or loss of interest.

In this series of cases characterized by diminution of interest in or response to the outside world, the material may be divided into three sub-groups.

Group II (a)

Patients presenting an anergic, indifferent or parasitic condition

Kirby has described patients with progressive loss of interest in external affairs and serious deterioration in conduct without any evidence of morbid ideas ("Dementia praecox deteriorations without trends"). These patients deserve the most careful review of their physical status, of early conditioning experiences, of underlying emotional and instinctive difficulties, of the actual life situation; the detailed histological study of the brain of such a patient is to be desired.

Several cases in our schizophrenic series were provisionally formulated in terms of a deterioration without trends, but in most cases a later review covering an extended period revealed important preoccupations and morbid ideas. In some cases there were only incidental and isolated morbid ideas while the lack of interest, spontaneity, and normal response to social values was striking. Such patients may be akin to those described by Kirby.

The following case (Olive P.) illustrates the problem presented by these patients. The patient, a waitress, was first admitted to the hospital at the age of twenty because she showed an unusual attitude to an illegitimate pregnancy. From childhood she had shown a rather disagreeable personality; at ten she had lost her mother, at twelve her father. She had witnessed and ruminated over erotic scenes between her father and housekeeper; after his death she was brought up in various foster homes. She had with difficulty scraped through high school, but was industrious and had literary ambitions. During her illegitimate pregnancy at twenty, she showed a striking apathy and lack of emotional response, seemed almost indif-

ferent to the situation, talked in an extremely
naïve way about sex; she preferred to stay in bed
till noon, spent her time reading and playing the
piano. In a home for expectant mothers her indifference to the coming event, her ambition to become a great artist, her strange seclusive behavior
and silly laughter alarmed the other girls; the
Intelligence Quotient was 88. After her child was
born she refused to surrender it, continued to pay
spasmodically for its maintenance but showed
little evidence of affection. After five further
seclusive years in the community at a low economic
level, with an indifferent attitude to crude sex
experiences, she was again in hospital on account
of day-dreaming spells of absorption during her
routine office work. In the hospital she talked of
her early sex preoccupations and of prolonged
masturbation, and developed the phantasy that
she was going to marry a ward physician; this
phantasy she continued to maintain in the hospital
to which she was transferred. Physical status not
noteworthy.

Thus we see a young woman of mediocre intelligence and poor social response, with sex
desire finding crude satisfaction without the
glamour of romance, carrying on a drab existence
without evidence of much emotional tension and

conflict and with a meager resort to imaginative activity, her interest in and response to the outside world occasionally sinking beneath the level required for normal conduct. Such a life history seems to be the product of inferior constitutional endowment and conditioning environmental factors.

In the following case the loss of interest in and response to the environment is again in the foreground and there occur only a few sporadic misinterpretations. The patient (Peter Q.), a lad of nineteen, had been brought up in an atmosphere of domestic discord; he had shown marked antagonism to his father, a man of suspicious, jealous, resentful nature. From childhood he was a rather unhappy and solitary boy, with few interests, inclined to play with younger children. He left school at fourteen, after an incident in which he was unjustly punished by the enraged parent of a school-mate. From this time he showed complete lack of interest in a personal career and avoided social contacts. He remained at home, did simple domestic tasks with no evidence of physical weakness. He spent his time in occasional solitary walks or attendance at the cinema. There was no overt evidence of preoccupation with sex. In hospital he admitted that there had been occasional masturbation, but he denied any interest in girls. Occasional utterances indicated a certain realization of and sensitiveness to his inferiority; thus he referred to something being wrong with his nerves, to being crazy; he suggested that his family laughed at him, and that the neighbors had dogs in their yards in order to tease him, that people made fun of his nose which he considered too big.

In the hospital he showed no initiative, took no interest in discussing his condition, thought that his stay in the hospital was futile. He admitted a feeling of inadequacy, complained that no one told him what to do. Eighteen months later when in another hospital he expressed the idea that he was under a spell; there was an episode of sleeplessness when he thought someone was after him, and he had shown some anger. There was no evidence of any bodily ailment, there was no history of any previous illness which might throw light on the condition.

This patient presented a striking lack of interest in and of response to the opportunities and the demands of the environment; in addition there was evidence of a continuing state of emotional tension of mild degree. He was sensitive, objected to people watching him eat; he had a vague feeling of discouragement and helplessness, leading to irritability and reproach ("no one was doing anything for him"; "the family didn't care for him").

A shipping clerk of twenty-four (Quentin R.), presented a similar condition of lack of interest and seclusiveness, but, in addition, more emotional tension than in the previous cases, and some eccentricity of conduct; internal conflicts gave rise to a disorder of mood and conduct with a negligible resort to morbid ideation.

The patient had during his school period shown less than average ability but he was a friendly individual, liked by others, and at first took part in the usual recreations, but did not dance; he had a slight lisp, was rather sensitive at school about being large for his age; about the time of leaving school he became addicted to masturbation and his father and brother had lectured him on the dire results of the habit. On leaving school at the end of the eighth grade, about thirteen, he worked steadily and with apparent satisfaction until he was twenty-one, when he was laid off on account of work being slack. He was said to be very nervous after an auto accident of uncertain date. About the age of nineteen, when the family moved away from their friends to a more pretentious neighborhood, he began to be seclusive, dropped his friends, ceased to take part in any social recreations. After he lost his regular job at twenty-one he had one summer job as waiter, then he ceased to make any effort to find work. After about two years at home, during which he was coöperative and willing to do odd jobs, he showed a change of mood and behavior, became sensitive and irritable. He became antagonistic to other members of the family except his mother, but one day he turned against her, grabbed her tightly in a way that alarmed the family. He laid somewhat undue emphasis on his father's mild alcoholism, wished his mother to get a divorce. About this period he felt that the neighbors were watching him, he kept the curtains down, wandered about the house only partly clad. In the hospital he complained of strange bodily feelings, which he attributed to masturbation. On one occasion he claimed that he saw two men looking at him through the transom. The patient was much more free and coöperative after a brief hospital visit; he spent the following year at home and showed more initiative, expressed no odd ideas. On account of his nervous condition seven months later he was readmitted to the hospital. He showed at

times an irritable and resentful attitude. He spoke
vaguely of nurses influencing his mind; at times
he would impulsively bang the walls and tables;
he mumbled to himself, at night called out to the
blank wall, but he emphatically denied having
hallucinations.

A market helper of twenty-six (Robert S.)
showed a similar abandonment of effort and acceptance of a parasitic existence but without any
evidence of emotional tension or of delusions. The
patient, brought up in a poor and discordant home,
had been normally sociable, full of fun; he had
had nothing to do with girls.

After working in a meat market for seven
years, about the age of twenty-three he talked
of being discouraged because he could save no
money; at twenty-four he gave up his job or perhaps was discharged; some time previously his
father had died. He now was forgetful, complained of insomnia and indigestion; he sat in the
house most of the time, preferred to be alone,
often laughed to himself, said this was due to his
thoughts. At the age of twenty-six he began to
neglect his appearance, went weeks without shav-
ing, would not bathe unless urged, commenced to
take exhausting walks, would apparently lose his

way. After being scolded by his mother for a trifle he wandered away from the house, was picked up by the police in a dazed condition. In the hospital he was seclusive and under-talkative, placid; said he was not depressed, "sort of happy." No morbid ideas could be elicited. During the following year in hospital and two further years at home his condition remained the same. No physical ailment was demonstrated.

While in the preceding cases the abandonment of effort and lack of response were unexplained by any overt difficulty, in the following case overt difficulties seemed to play an important rôle; physical factors may also have made their contribution. The patient (Sylvia T.), thirty-one years of age, had from girlhood been preoccupied with a facial disfigurement. She was much discouraged by an ineffective operation to improve her appearance. For several years after leaving school she had a few simple jobs, also studied music. For several years before admission she had lived alone with her mother, the father an orthodox and tyrannical patriarch having left the home, the other sisters having married. The patient had always been sensitive and rather seclusive, but during the latter years she had almost confined herself to the house; she seemed to take no interest in home affairs or in her personal appearance, she resented the interference of her mother. She would not eat if anyone were around, she talked little and in a whisper. She felt that her physical health was poor due to abscessed teeth and infected tonsils, but that her mental state was normal. A second tonsillectomy had not improved her condition. In hospital the patient was uncoöperative, made no spontaneous remarks, talked in a whisper; she explained that her conduct had been due to infected teeth and tonsils, she insisted that her right ear be x-rayed as it was turning to bone. She claimed that she was happy, admitted no mental disorder, claimed that her behavior was her own business, desired to be left alone.

The patient was under-nourished, her teeth had much dentistry which was in fair condition; the throat was clear, but there was much hawking and some spitting; no evidence of pulmonary disorder was found.

The patient was allowed to make a trial visit home, but was so antagonistic to her people that she was again admitted to a mental hospital. There she was very uncommunicative, at times refused to eat; after eight months she still refused to talk to the doctors and nurses but voiced complaints to her mother; she occasionally made grimaces. She was well nourished and apparently in good physical health. Two years later with no change in her mental state save periods of irritability she began to lose weight, signs of pulmonary tuberculosis were observed and four months later the patient died.

In the following case a prolonged, perhaps permanent, slump in output of energy and in social contacts was accompanied by odd motor activity and by philosophical ruminations, without distortion of the outside world.

The patient (Thomas U.), a salesman of twenty-nine, the second of seven children, had made a good school record but left in the first year of high school on account of the necessity of helping his widowed mother, his father having died when the patient was eight years old. The patient was a sociable, cheerful and efficient worker; he had one lukewarm love affair at twenty-six. At twenty-eight, owing to the general economic situation, he lost his job. Two months after this he became over-religious, going to church several times a day. He then began to be silent and to avoid his friends. For six months before admission he had not spoken spontaneously, he had answered in monosyllables; he made no effort to find work.

In the hospital he complied with the routine, showed no interest in other persons, answered briefly and made very few spontaneous remarks. He preferred to be by himself and he was seen to carry out peculiar movements of stereotyped nature which he called "gymnastics." He said that he was not depressed, that he had nothing on his mind and was contented. At the same time he said that he was just overworked, discouraged. He knew that he was in a mental hospital, showed no worry about the future, said that he would work after his discharge. He seemed to have no realization of the reason for his being admitted to the hospital. He claimed that he was mentally sound. The patient admitted that he spent much time in ethical and philosophical ruminations of rather empty and formal nature. He made vague statements about hearing his own thoughts, but no other evidence of hallucinations could be elicited.

The patient was transferred to another hospital and during the following two years his general behavior showed little change. During one interview, however, during this period, the physician made the note that the patient expressed himself in a very odd way. The patient during this period had made several visits at home where he expressed no odd ideas and did nothing peculiar, but showed the same curious lack of interest and spontaneity, without any evidence of depression. The patient semed to be quite content with his hospital existence.

To summarize tentatively the outstanding features in the group of patients just reviewed: the patients, of mediocre intelligence, socially rather passive and without keen interest in practicable goals, with limited sex desire and little ability to establish wholesome relations with the other sex, at a certain stage of life abandon effort, become socially isolated and individually unproductive. In their indifferent or discouraged parasitic existence, with or without evidence of impatience, resentment, reproach, they leave their personal maintenance and care to the initiative of others; they do not resort to crude erotism or infantile habits; they construct no compensatory delusions, or do so only in an episodic and very simple way.

Group II (b)

Patients presenting a stuporous syndrome

While in the above cases the inaccessibility and unproductivity of the patients are in the setting of a lack of energy, of interest, of spontaneity, with discouragement and sensitiveness but little evidence of emotional tension, without clouding of thought and with little misinterpretation of the outside world, in the following cases of inaccessibility and unproductivity there is more emotional tension, sometimes crude tendencies break through to the surface, thought is more disturbed.

In some such cases of marked lack of response the review of the personality and of the life situation may make the clinical picture intelligible as the reaction to an overt difficulty. Thus a young woman, whose engagement had been ruthlessly terminated by her parents, after a brief period of restless agitation and sleeplessness passed into a prolonged stupor with complete neglect of the environment and inattention to personal cleanliness, from which condition she gradually emerged to resume her interrupted career.

In other cases underlying stresses and strains, not clearly recognized by the patient, may possibly play the same etiological rôle as overt difficulties.

Inaccessibility and withdrawal of interest are frequently a phase of the clinical picture in Group I; in the following series of cases these symptoms are a much more prominent and protracted feature. While in this tentative and preliminary classification we consider together cases with a period of pronounced or protracted inaccessibility, there is no guarantee that these cases do more than present in rather striking form a mode of reaction which may also play a part in cases of somewhat different evolution. The psychiatrist who has been compelled for administrative reasons to use a formal Kraepelinian classification has distributed his cases between the hebephrenic and the catatonic groups only with compunction.

In the following cases, along with reduction of interest in the workaday world, one sees turmoil in the emotional and instinctive life, tension, feelings of inferiority, of guilt and shame, and behavior indicating the urgency of the crude sex appetite and of pleasure-seeking tendencies of infantile nature.

The first case is that of a stenographer of twenty-one (Ursula V.), the fourth of eight children, who had graduated from high school with distinction and had been an efficient

stenographer until she was laid off on account of
the general economic situation. She had never had
any love affair, she brushed the topic of marriage
aside, showed no overt curiosity about sex mat-
ters. She was a quiet, shy and rather sensitive
girl, never talking much about her own inner life,
giving no indication of any personal problems.

At the age of seventeen the patient had a period
of depression with sudden onset and abrupt recovery. She seemed to have ideas of unworthiness
during this period ("What good am I?"). At the
age of twenty for a period of several months she
avoided meeting visitors and finally after a
peculiar emotional episode she became stuporous.
In the hospital a few days after this spell the
patient was perplexed and apprehensive, talked in
a very fragmentary way, was not clear as to the
nature of the hospital, misidentified those around
her, did not know the date, not being able to give
either the month or the year; "I can't remember
a thing." The patient coöperated very poorly.
She had ideas of unworthiness; "I'm bad," "I
sinned to my mother and father," "I'm making
you suffer more." She misidentified those around
her as members of her family or as moving picture stars; "I'm all mixed up. I want to tell the
truth and I can't." After this first interview the

patient was practically inaccessible to any ordinary attempt at conversation. Occasionally she
said to a nurse that she was ashamed of herself.
During the administration of various percentages
of carbon dioxide in the weeks following admission the patient was more talkative. She admitted
a sense of guilt which seemed to be associated
with autoerotism. She talked of infatuation for
her brother and for an old teacher.

During the following year the patient continued
to show very little contact with those around her;
for a long period she wet and soiled herself. For
many months she did not speak but at times
she would communicate by writing. She expressed
a hatred for men, said that they were dirty; she
wrote that she hated a young man, who had come
into her bedroom, that she liked her brother, that
she had sinned against her parents. She also admitted autoerotism previous to admission.

After a year in the hospital the patient showed
very marked development of erotic activity,
masturbating very frequently, exposing herself,
making advances to the physicians. She also wet
and soiled herself. She began to be impulsive and
aggressive and became very difficult to look after.
She gave up communication by writing.

The patient was transferred to another hospital

and there she continued during the following year to present periods of extreme excitement, with great difficulty of management.

A backward but ambitious girl of twenty (Viola W.) had always been very sensitive to the fact that she was inferior to her brilliant younger sister. She observed silently her sister's success with men but she maintained an overt refusal to have anything to do with them and professed to dislike their company, saying "I may be backward but I'm a lady." She was self-assertive, resented correction.

At the age of twenty rather acutely she showed peculiar behavior in her position as nursemaid. She was very silent, thought that people on the street noticed her, was irritable. In the hospital she was uncommunicative, talked in monosyllables, showed unexplained emotional reactions. She claimed that she had heard voices for two weeks; they said silly things such as "sweetie," "nice girl," "she is too perfect, better than anybody else," but they also said that she was only a servant. She accepted the suggestion that these voices might be her imagination. The patient was quite clear in her grasp of the environment and showed no defect in memory. She appeared to have no in-

sight into her condition. The patient was a girl
of asthenic type, poorly nourished, with extremi-
ties somewhat cyanotic; she had complained of
heart trouble, there were occasional extra systoles.

After a few days in the hospital the patient was
taken home, but after several months was admitted to another mental hospital. During the following three years she seemed to be quite out of
touch with the environment. At periods she was
mute, at other times she would scream loudly like
a child. She struck herself and assaulted others.
She masturbated persistently, tended to expose
herself. She appeared to have hallucinations of
hearing.

A third patient, an intelligent girl of seventeen
(Winifred X.), was brought up in a sordid home
with illiterate parents and many defective and
delinquent siblings. Two months before admission
she missed a period, complained of not feeling
well; she gave up her factory work, became quiet
and seclusive, stayed much in bed, thought that
people were against her (an idea partly based on
her mother's reaction to the amenorrhoea).

In hospital she was almost inaccessible and was
taken away in a few days, but three weeks later
was admitted to a state hospital in a condition of

stupor. During the following months she was mute, resistive, assaulted others, occasionally disrobed, but after five months she became neater and more agreeable. One year after the onset of symptoms she seemed to have recovered, but two years later she was reported to require hospital treatment again.

A secretary, thirty years of age (Yvonne Z.), the daughter of a catatonic mother, had been brought up in a very unusual home atmosphere; at school although given a strict conventional code, she indulged in autoerotic and possibly homosexual activity. An unsuitable love affair and inconsiderate criticism by her employer had upset her before admission. She abandoned her work, said she was unworthy to live, refused food, retained her urine and faeces.

In the hospital she appeared confused, perplexed, afraid. She felt dead, she had committed a crime, voices condemned her, her body did not feel natural, it no longer belonged to her. She stated that the symptoms had developed after she had abandoned autoerotism. For months the patient showed an absorbed appearance, answered no questions, showed no spontaneity, smiled and laughed to herself; for a period she walked and

stood on tiptoe. During the major part of her
nine months' stay in hospital she wet and soiled
herself. During the last month she was cleanly and
showed marked improvement, but still heard
voices; ten months after leaving hospital she was
reported to be free from positive abnormalities,
but to be lethargic, dependent, babyish, with no
interest in resuming work.

A high school girl of sixteen (Alice B.), always
bashful, quiet and seclusive, with no interest in
athletics or in the other sex, complained of being
blue, became very seclusive, stayed alone both in
the house and when out on the beach. During the
autumn she protested against returning to school,
frequently avoided going to school by going back
to bed in the morning. After one month she gave
up school and spent most of her time in bed.
She claimed that she was dizzy and unable to hold
her head up; she wept frequently. She complained
of people looking at her and talking about her.
She passed water frequently, occasionally wet herself. For three years she had been accustomed to
spend an unusual time in the bathroom.

In the hospital the patient was shy and somewhat distressed and discouraged. She talked of
her thoughts being so vivid that she almost seemed

to hear them. There had been mild compulsive phenomena. The patient recognized her increasing seclusiveness and lack of interest. She complained that her mind was blank and that she could not be interested in anything. She complained of lack of ability to concentrate. She seemed to see things through a sort of fine mist and found herself compelled to stare at things. There had been apparently a certain amount of worry over masturbation. The patient felt somewhat estranged from her parents, day-dreamed of moving in a distinguished circle, felt superior to her actual acquaintances. After a few days in the hospital the patient showed somewhat dramatic emotional behavior and empty giggling; she seemed absorbed, rather ecstatic; she said she was in love with the physician, thought that he controlled her. She asked questions about babies, gave crude sexual invitations, behaved in an erratic way. Her talk was disconnected. The patient showed no serious and continuous contact with the physician, her behavior was one of superficial playfulness with giggling and smiling in response to all questions. The patient during the following four years in a mental hospital showed no resumption of normal interests and contact with others; she remained superficial, was aggressive to the other patients, untidy and destructive. On one occasion she scalded her hands to prevent masturbation, she smeared herself and other patients with faeces. On one occasion when riding she placed her finger in her rectum. No mention of delusions was made in the report; she admitted hallucinations of hearing, sight, smell.

A sixth patient during a long incipient stage of her mental disorder showed recurrent periods of seclusiveness and loss of energy; later she passed into a condition characterized by a variable mood of extraordinary shallowness with ability to do simple work in a tolerant environment. A shy, sensitive and sober child (Beatrice C.), she had later worked as a telephone operator; there had been no overt expression of interest in the other sex, she recoiled from discussion of the topic of sex with the physician, but admitted masturbation from the age of twenty. At the age of twenty-six she began to have periods when she was slow at her work; she was sensitive about this, thought her superiors were critical of her. One year later there was a period when she was slow in her speech; she cut short a visit to a relative as she thought that the latter had put ground glass in her food. About this time on one occasion under a press of work she showed explosive emotion, struck at her immediate superior. During the following two years she limped along at her work, was cranky, tended to brood, had vacant spells, was sensitive; she referred much to right and wrong. Always devout and a daily churchgoer she tried to enter a convent but was rejected. She was admitted to the hospital after jumping from a window in order to go to church, and because life was not worth living. In the hospital she showed little spontaneity, unexplained smiling and laughter; she was fairly coöperative. In her rather superficial and disconnected talk she showed no dominant trend, made reference to sexual, perhaps incestuous, experiences, but chiefly talked of trifling and everyday topics. She denied that she had hallucinations but her conduct belied this.

During the following four years, partly at home, partly in a mental hospital, she was seclusive and rather indifferent, smiled and laughed but said that she was terribly worried. The following note is characteristic:

"Dear Ma: Just a few lines to say that I am going to commit suicide. Your loving daughter (here the signature). For Jesus Christ sake come to see me. They are treating me terrible. Bring me home to Pa." She was able to be utilized for simple domestic work.

In the following case erotic phantasies and physical complaints play a prominent rôle.

The patient (Cora D.), a stenographer, twenty-two years of age, had from girlhood been quiet, seclusive, shy, sensitive, rather conceited. She had been as a child rather capricious in regard to food. At the age of sixteen she had a definite tantrum in order to be allowed to go to the moving pictures. Between the ages of twenty and twenty-two she again had definite tantrums. She had one love affair at fifteen. At seventeen she had a boy friend who visited her regularly. She was capricious in her treatment of him, maintaining a rather cold attitude although much interested in his attentions. During the following years she did some stenographic work but was critical of her associates. She was quite self-centered, showed a good deal of irritability. She was rather peevish and complained of feeling bad. She received a good deal of medical attention about this time on account of her general complaints and discontent.

When examined in hospital at the age of twenty-two she was rather languid and peevish, harped on a variety of pains. Although her

mood was generally sober, she occasionally made
facetious remarks. She told of her love affair and
said that since her friend had given up visiting
her she had indulged in erotic phantasies about
him, and had let her mind dwell on sexual imagery.
She admitted erotic play in childhood and autoerotism in adult life. She recognized that she was
in a disturbed state of mind, said she had
"complete dementia."

During a stay of a few months in the hospital
she was very much preoccupied with herself,
ruminated over her symptoms both mental and
physical and felt that she had to get rid of "a
certain feeling." No evidence of hallucinations or
delusions; memory and general information unimpaired. She was seclusive, at times was quite
unwilling to take part in ward activities, on one
occasion had a screaming attack and kicked the
nurse.

When transferred to another hospital she made
the statement that someone had given her poison
and she claimed that she saw faces. She refused
food and was profane at times. She was negativistic, irritable, uncommunicative. On one occasion she tried to bite the nurse. She said that she
was in love with the physician and day-dreamed
about him. After five months she was transferred

to another hospital and there she was very un-communicative with the physician, harped on go-ing home, at times was silly in behavior and was described as "untidy and fighting when attempt is made to clean her up." Apparently she showed this untidiness on more than one occasion.

After a period at home she was again admitted to a state hospital and for the following two years she remained in an apathetic condition. As a rule she was seclusive, at times impulsive. She showed a shallow emotional reaction; she uttered a few delusional ideas such as that at home telephone calls had been withheld from her, the people downstairs wanted to get rid of her; she claimed that she heard auto horns outside and that she saw pictures in marks on the wall. She had some insight into her condition, saying that there was "something out of her brain."

The material so far presented shows that among those schizophrenic cases with serious lack of contact with the workaday world (Group II) one can separate one group (a) presenting an anergic syndrome, and a second group (b) in which inaccessibility is associated with tension, impulsive aggression, and the expression of crude erotic trends. In these two groups the formation

of delusions plays a minor rôle; the outstanding
feature is the gross modification of the dynamics
of the individual, not the disorder of the symbolizing activity.

Group II (c)

*Patients presenting reduction of interest with dis-
tortion of the outside world*

In other cases where loss of interest and
seclusiveness are early symptoms there is less
urgency of crude erotic trends, while distorted
ideas of the outside world are more in evidence.

In the following case the distorted ideas develop in the setting of an emotional episode after
a long period of deterioration of interest and of
behavior.

The patient (Doris E.), a clerical worker,
thirty-one years of age, had during her girlhood
shown no special seclusiveness but had been as
active socially as the average girl of her age. During adolescence she did simple clerical work and
showed a tendency to feel that fellow workers disliked her. About the age of twenty she showed
increasing seclusiveness, lack of interest in ordinary affairs, pretentious literary activity; she

felt confident that she would become a famous authoress. She lost a job on account of inefficiency and since then had only occasional work for brief periods. The patient had shown no special interest in the other sex. At the age of twenty-seven when a younger sister was about to be married the patient was sensitive about this fact, left home, made an abrupt marriage to a worthless man, left him after two months, reappeared half starved and ill-clad. Seven months later a stillborn child was born; she seemed quite indifferent. From this time on the patient lived a rather dilapidated life, occasionally leaving home without obvious reason. She lost all nicety of manners and interest in her personal appearance, was seclusive, sat for hours staring into space. Apparently her pretentious ambitions persisted. At the age of thirty-one she got a job in a factory but complained that the workers were hostile to her.

On admission to the hospital the patient seemed somewhat anxious and apprehensive. She denied being depressed but said that she was frightened. She told of disquieting experiences of a rather vague type. People seemed to be hostile to her, made threatening gestures and uttered threatening words, passed death threats. She had such experiences from casual people in the subway, from the foreman in the factory, from the people in the employment bureau. She had, therefore, gone to an immigration office in order to be deported to some other country (she was born in the United States). People were trying to degrade her. She said that her family were only her foster relatives.

After a week in the hospital the patient was much less tense and apprehensive and returned to her family. In this case the history is similar to that of Olive P. (p. 82), with the addition of the delusional formation.

In the following case the period of seclusiveness was less prolonged and less extreme and the morbid ideas seemed to be much more persistent although difficult to elicit.

The patient (Earl F.), aged twenty-four, a student, had been brought up in an extraordinary home atmosphere, the mother, although paranoid and a spiritualist, supporting the household, the father being out of work. The patient was a rather quiet, dreamy lad, teased by his schoolmates; he made few friends, had a satisfactory school record. At the age of fifteen he had two attacks of unconsciousness but no evidence of convulsive movements. Several attempts at a college career

were unsatisfactory. He took up aviation but had
to discontinue it on account of finances. During
this period of his life he made no friendships,
attended no social affairs. At the age of twenty-
three he began to be apathetic, more seclusive and
irritable. He indulged in masturbation and showed
little emotional reaction when detected. One evening at a friend's house he passed into some sort
of trance and claimed that God had him in control. He talked later of the subconscious mind
and of the truth of psychic control, ideas very
familiar to him from his mother's outlook. He
claimed that a dead sweetheart had been speaking
to him and that he saw her. A few days later he
asked his mother to get a gun as his father was
going to shoot her. He accused his mother of
hypnotizing his father. He received spiritualistic
communications and saw visions.

In the hospital the patient was restless and
preoccupied but communicative; he showed a mixture of friendliness and irritability. He told of the
voices that he had been hearing for the last three
weeks; they were from the astral sphere. These
experiences were somewhat fragmentary and did
not seem to be concerned with any special topic
of preoccupation. He did not think that people
were against him but anxiously requested that his

mother be released; she was being mesmerized and injured. The patient during his two weeks in hospital showed restless and preoccupied behavior.

He returned home where he continued to express fragmentary delusions. Some months later he was admitted to another hospital. There he was apparently preoccupied with his own ideas which were grandiose, religious, sexual. He continued to hear voices. He was extremely seclusive, uncommunicative and uncoöperative at first. After several months his general behavior had improved very much so that he was able to return home. After a trial period at home he was readmitted to a state hospital. At this time he was very restless and talkative with flight of ideas. He destroyed the sheets and assaulted other patients. The exact trend of his ideas was not determined.

Two years later, during a period of treatment in another state hospital, his condition was very much the same and his lack of coöperation made it difficult to determine the content of his ideas.

The young woman, whose case follows, showed marked withdrawal of interest from the workaday world, little overt evidence of crude sex urge, impulsive assaults, hallucinations, delusional fragments. The patient (Frances G.) had been brought up in a home of discord, the unstable and unreliable mother openly accusing the father of infidelity and incestuous relations with the patient. The patient went through the second year of high school; she was not particularly seclusive but in the teens she was teased by her schoolmates on account of her preoccupation with her madonna-like appearance. To her sister she admitted worry over masturbation. At sixteen, after a boy had discontinued his attentions, she became silent, for three months she remained in bed. During the following two years she twice remained away from school for a month. For some months before admission to a hospital at the age of nineteen she avoided taking her meals with the family, and two weeks before admission she remained in bed with her head covered, refused to talk; after a week of this behavior she developed an exhilarated excitement, had hallucinations—"they are getting me now, consuming my body—hear them in the wall." She then became stuporous.

In the hospital the patient lay in bed with face covered, resisted the attention of the nurses. She smiled in a queer way. She answered few questions, gave no information as to her mood; she admitted that she heard voices, they discussed movies, said pleasant things. She was only approximately oriented. There was nothing noteworthy in the physical status. Transferred to another hospital the patient during the following year was preoccupied, apathetic, at times resistive and impulsively aggressive, occasionally was tube-fed. She was unkempt, "untidy both in bed and in the day room." At times she had spells of empty staring into space. After about a year she was allowed to go home where her childish condition necessitated supervision; the development of a stuporous condition required her return to the hospital. During the visit at home she had a period when she had a morbid belief that the cooking utensils and drinking water were dirty; there had also been a period of alternative laughter and crying. During the following three years she continued to be dull and apathetic, at times stood gazing into space, occasionally showed unprovoked outbursts of violence. From the beginning of the marked symptoms five years previously she had complained of lights, had buried her head under the clothes. At this later period she would not tolerate a light, broke all light bulbs, at times tore down the wiring. She seemed to hear voices, at times talked to herself in an excited manner.

The distortion of the outer world in the following case takes the form chiefly of hallucinatory experiences, with sparse delusional interpretations. An Italian girl (Grace H.) had been brought up by her insane mother until the age of eight; from the age of ten she lived in various homes; part of the time she lived alone with her alcoholic father, at twelve she told a teacher of his incestuous approaches. Some time later she admitted masturbation and erotic dreams. She was placed in a foster home and some months later, while in the seventh grade at thirteen, she became moody, went around with head bowed, had laughing spells. She later said that one of the children had called her bad names, she did not give details—"I don't want to tell, news spreads all over the world." Admitted to the hospital at the age of fourteen she was superficially coöperative, gave little insight into her inner life; she said that people on the street had taken undue notice of her feet as if she walked funny. On two occasions she had heard a song within her head; this had made her laugh. The patient was oriented, with good memory and fair store of general information; her Intelligence Quotient was 78%. Nothing noteworthy in the physical status.

Placed in another foster home she continued to

make rather poor progress in school. She was a devout attendant at church but now she began to have laughing spells in church; she said that the altar boys made dirty remarks to her, and that the priest reprimanded them (no confirmation of this). She said that she wanted to be a saint. The religious behavior of the patient recalled the behavior of her insane mother when the patient was between six and eight years of age. One day the patient screamed so that the neighbors were disturbed; she said that she had heard voices, seen things. She made vague physical complaints. As to these hallucinations she said, "You can hear them as well as I can."

In the hospital, now almost fifteen years of age, she was very uncommunicative; she denied that she was depressed, admitted the auditory hallucinations, gave no details; a complete mental examination was impossible. Her physical status was satisfactory. During the following months in hospital the patient maintained the above condition; she was very uncoöperative, needed to be urged to eat, had occasional unexplained outbursts of laughter; she harped on going home. She continued to hear voices which encouraged her to be good. During thyroid treatment there was a brief period of exhilaration and overactivity. The patient was transferred to another hospital. After a short stay there she was placed in a foster home where at first she was apathetic, required much personal care, occasionally wet herself, but for a time became a happy and agreeable member of the household. After a few months she relapsed, became less cleanly, had a tantrum, was readmitted to the hospital. She said that she heard people telling her mystery stories and fairy stories about herself; these stories made her laugh. During the following two years the patient's state became worse. She became negativistic, required effort to get her to eat, did little or no work, frequently had excited periods, was noted as "definitely catatonic—had no regard for sphincter control—showed a few auto-mutilative tendencies." The last note described her as untidy, destructive, quarrelsome, disoriented with defective memory; she continued to have hallucinations.

In the first group (Group I) of schizophrenic cases which we have discussed, emotional turmoil and unsystematized disturbance of behavior were prominent features in the clinical picture.

The patients in the second group (Group II) were characterized by withdrawal of interest from the outside world, by apathy or by tension with episodic outbursts; hallucinations were frequently present, delusions played a small part in the total clinical picture. Little of the inner life of the patient was revealed to the physician owing to inaccessibility.

Group III

Patients with a distorted world picture

In a third group of cases now to be discussed the most prominent feature is the development of a distorted picture of the outside world. This feature is by no means confined to this group nor are the clinical symptoms of the previous groups altogether foreign to this third group. In the former two groups the individual has greater recourse to the more fundamental mechanisms of the instinctive and the emotional life. In this third group the patients make fuller use of the thought processes, more subtle mechanisms for maintaining personal equilibrium in the setting of the total situation. The turmoil in the first group, the inaccessibility in the second group, make it difficult to analyze in detail the dynamic situation. In this third group also one may meet special difficulties in reconstructing the inner life of the individual; even when the patient is accessible the strange and incongruous nature of the patient's outlook on the world, the frequently fragmentary nature of its presentation, the curious twists of phrase, the unfamiliar verbal symbols may present no inconsiderable barrier between the physician and the patient. This third group may for convenience be provisionally subdivided into further sub-groups, and to illustrate three sub-groups some cases will be given.

Group III (a)

Patients with wish-fulfilling phantasies

In the first sub-group the distorted picture of the outside world is largely dominated by the wish-fulfilling function of thought. Phantasy is called on to supply what real life has denied, but the phantasies are not woven into a structure which is compatible with normal social adaptation. The origin of the phantasies may not be difficult to trace. It is not so easy to understand the abeyance of the critical faculty; some may consider that this defect of judgment must indicate some fundamental destructive process which has to be formulated at the physiological level; others may consider that even in the absence of such underlying process the actual life situation may be so

intolerable to the individual with his special needs
that he discards the attempt at a realistic adaptation, but instead of a passive and anergic surrender
he seeks a tolerable adaptation by means of
phantasy or autistic thought. In face of a world
which is intolerable, if constructed according to
the canons conventionally insisted on for the
practical purposes of community life, the individual rejects these canons, insists on the right to
personal satisfaction, ignores the data which cannot be assimilated, creates through phantasy the
factors which are essential for the satisfaction of
his needs.

A carpenter, twenty-nine years of age (Harry
I.), had shown an uneventful childhood. He had
been a good scholar, left in the third year of high
school to help to support the family. He had
always regretted being unable to proceed to college, and felt inferior in relation to many of his
associates who had had this privilege. As a boy
he had masturbated until the age of fifteen when
a scout book had persuaded him that masturbation
leads to insanity. He appeared normal in his
friendships and outdoor activities, was rather
serious, liked to remain at home and to read
serious books. He did not care much about going

out, he could not be persuaded to attend a dance. His physical health was good but his mother laid much emphasis on a gastric upset which had preceded the psychosis by several months. The first symptoms developed when he was working away from home; he began to lose weight, his landlady noticed that he was restless, slept poorly, walked the floor. On his return home he found that he could not concentrate on his work, he remained at home, worried about losing his mind, asked his mother to pray for him. He said that he had seen God in church, he talked a good deal about some girl whom he had casually met on the bus on the journey home.

In the hospital the patient showed a certain degree of depression, was rather restless, his memory and grasp of general information were satisfactory. He was dominated by morbid ideas which concerned religion and marriage. In his utterances the topics of love, of his personal value, of his social status, were prominent. He never was able to present a systematic or clear account of the forces which he seemed to postulate in the outside world. The following utterances give a good sample of the fragmentary presentation of his preoccupations: "They wanted me to get married—different fathers wanted it. I did not want to leave the Church—because I thought I was doing something for Father Church; so I said to the girl—and then I told her that I was interested in art—so we had a conversation like that—A Christian can't be a philosopher—natural artist—not in true love—I didn't want to give up the Church. I will say that there has been some miracles—If I had worn my good clothes I would have married her." He had heard someone in a dream say "The Holy Nun is pining for you— that is better than being an artist—you are a saint now." The patient was quite persuaded that this girl whom he had seen on the bus was destined to be his wife and this union apparently had special religious sanction: "I did not sacrifice the Church —so this girl, her party—they want me to compromise, they arranged a sitting in the Catholic Church—they said something—I did not know what to do. To be venerated as the most perfect love—that does not sound right. I wanted to marry the girl then—a saint getting married like that seemed so darned funny." Voices had said "he is not guilty," "she is all right," "you love your mother," "don't forget the Church."

During the following two months the patient's preoccupations became less prominent and faded into the background. The patient took part in the normal activities of the ward and wished to dismiss the memory of his previous ideas. He was able to be at home for a few months. He then began to remain in the house and to talk strangely. He said that the priests were trying to make a saint of him, the politicians were going to make him president, the newspapers were making public his residence in a mental hospital. The patient was readmitted to the hospital and during the following six months he showed the same preoccupation with morbid ideas, maintaining that the church and the newspapers were interested in him, that people wanted to make him a saint. He was also preoccupied in a dreamlike way with the topic of marriage and with the personality of the girl whom he had casually met. Notwithstanding these ideas, the patient was a quiet, pleasant and friendly member of the hospital group, showing a rather unusual placidity.

A similar combination of poorly elaborated religious and erotic phantasies is shown by the following case.

The patient, a factory worker of twenty-two (Mary Q.), had been brought up in an extremely devout household, one aunt having taken holy orders. The patient was said to have been somewhat nervous from infancy. There was an early history of nail-biting, nose-picking, bed-wetting. She had been somewhat fidgety, impulsive in her actions. In later girlhood she was self-willed, resented direction, was careless about her personal appearance, liable to leave tasks half done. From childhood she had been imaginative and loved to identify herself with the heroines of romantic novels. She was looked upon as quite social but had a very limited group of friends. She never had any boy friends and never went out to dances or mixed parties. The subject of sex was practically never discussed in the family. The patient admitted to the physicians later that she had practised autoerotism since about the age of fifteen. The possibility of following in the footsteps of her aunt, the nun, was familiar to the patient in childhood.

The patient went for two years to high school. She then took up work in a factory. At the age of nineteen she entered a convent. After two years mental symptoms made it necessary for her to leave the convent. She returned to factory work where she proved to be a misfit and unable to do the work. She was now more forgetful than she had previously been, was unable to concentrate and was easily upset.

In the hospital the patient was coöperative, showed a placid and rather indifferent attitude, presented no special anomaly of behavior. There was no evidence of definite depression, her mood seemed to be rather one of apathy. She was much preoccupied with her special experiences and ruminated over various topics. She said that even before she entered the convent she had occasionally heard the voice of God, she had wondered if a certain priest were actually God. In the convent one night after looking at a picture of the bleeding heart of Christ she felt that the heart was throbbing. In the chapel she saw the lips of a statue of the Virgin move and heard a voice say comforting words. A voice said to her, "I want you to be my mother." "Could it be true that I was to have a baby—I thought the infant in her arms spoke, I thought I might give birth to Christ." The patient stated that she was going to be the wife of a future ruler of the world. This was in order to prepare herself for her destiny as Mother of God. The patient had some insight into the imaginative source of her ideas: "When reading the life of anyone you will follow it and think how wonderful it would be to be that person, and if you stretch your imagination you think you are going to become one like it. It made me think that

I was the person, the Holy Virgin. It was sort of a mixture of religion with natural thoughts. My thoughts got mixed with thoughts about being the Mother of God." The patient had the idea that she was a dual personality. She seemed to have a good deal of insight into the significance of this dual personality, stating that the younger self represented various unfulfilled desires: "With the younger self I thought I could do the things I would have done when younger. The old self was on the right side, the new self on the left." The patient admitted much erotic revery. She said that several times she felt that her body was slightly elevated while in bed, she felt something pressing on her and the movements of coitus. It looked ethereal like a white cloud. The experience was so clean that this must have been God. She claimed that she was the bride of Christ.

The patient spent several months in this placid day-dreaming existence, the ideas for a time fading but then returning. An attempt to live outside and to take some training was a complete failure as she was unable to concentrate or do the simplest task. She was later transferred to a state hospital and during the following three years continued to lead a day-dreaming existence, preoccupied with the same topics as before. God spoke to her, she was three Marys, the Mary of twelve, the other Mary of twenty-three (herself), and Mary the Mother of God. She claimed that she had the power to heal the ills of other people. At the end of three years the patient was very untidy in her habits, could not be induced to occupy herself, was impulsive. She would stare into space in an absent way, at times would laugh without apparent reason. She made random statements, e.g. "Christmas is celebrated today" (September), "a dollar contains five nickels." The patient was described as noisy, crying easily and "violent to herself."

Other cases show how the topic of sex and of its religious sanctification may give rise to a great variety of delusions of simple or complicated nature. The following case exemplifies a rather simple resort to phantasy.

The patient, a young woman of nineteen (Jane K.), brought up in the shadow of a rather alert twin sister, had been rather dull at school, was discouraged by an unsympathetic teacher, was not very efficient in her factory work. She had been brought up by an aunt, had received no sex instruction, was very unsophisticated on the topic, saw her attractive twin sister surrounded by beaux. On one occasion the patient was very much frightened and reported that she had been chased by some man. Two years later, at the age of nineteen, she became rather seclusive and claimed that she was going to have a baby, making the episode two years previous responsible for this.

When admitted to the hospital she was placid and coöperative, was very much preoccupied with the topic of her assumed pregnancy. She said that two years previously she had prayed for a baby. She knew little about conception, said that she thought babies came from heaven. She showed no other morbid beliefs, admitted no hallucinations. She was clearly oriented, her memory was not very precise. On her next menstruation the patient claimed that she had given up the idea that she was pregnant.

When transferred to another hospital she showed some restlessness and anxiety, talked in a somewhat resigned way, seemed to think that some trick had been played on her. She was not sure about her own name. She again claimed that she was pregnant. During the following two years the patient showed indolent and apathetic behavior with little interest in her surroundings, paid little attention to her personal appearance; she took little interest in interviews, answered in an irrelevant way. She did not seem to grasp the nature of her environment. She seemed to admit that she sometimes heard messages from heaven. One year later her condition showed little change. She would not talk during interviews, stared at the examiner without answering, laughed without apparent reason, gave her age as nineteen (her age at the onset of the psychosis).

A married woman of thirty (Joyce L.), who had never experienced sexual satisfaction in her married life, became interested in a man who visited her several times and who asked her to visit his apartment, which she refused to do. The patient became preoccupied with the thought of this man, was afraid that he might enter her room. One morning she claimed that she had been sexually assaulted during the night under the influence of chloroform. She made other detailed statements about this incident. During the following night the patient and her sister were both in a panic lest there might be a recurrence of this alleged occurrence, and on the following day the patient was brought to the hospital. The patient was in a somewhat emotional condition and talked in a confused and incoherent way. She made the statement that she had been to Hollywood, that the man referred to had altered her physically in various ways, that she had either had a baby or was going to have one. She was evidently much preoccupied with her erotic phantasies. Her mood varied from elation to perplexity and distress. She claimed that she was a moving picture star and boasted of having various accomplishments. The patient was oriented, had good memory and gave a good account of her life. Her married life had been unsatisfactory in every way, failing to meet her ambitions as well as her biological needs. The patient had a very slight elevation of temperature for which no cause was found in the physical examination.

During the week after admission the patient showed variable behavior, was perplexed and confused, at times stared emptily into space, showed impulsive reactions such as scratching another patient's eyes; in explanation she said, "My father hypnotized and tried to kill me, he wanted to scratch my eyes out." She said that she was not a man, but again she asked, "Am I homosexual?"

Transferred to another hospital the patient remained somewhat apathetic or depressed and perplexed, was still preoccupied with the idea of the attack and with her own identity as that of a moving picture star. After two years the patient was still in the hospital. She claimed that she was not married as she had not her wedding ring. She denied that her child was really her child. She reproached herself for the habit of autoerotism.

Phantasy may be mobilized to deal with other problems than those presented by the sexual urge and the craving for spiritual value. The desire for status and prestige may also lead to the development of compensatory phantasies.

A young student of twenty-nine (Leo M.), with poor family history, had been brought up in an uncongenial home atmosphere; his intolerant father and dominating sisters were felt as a serious restriction. As a boy he indulged in autoerotism with no special worry over it according to his own statement. A friend wrote, "he holds sex in utter abhorrence and has never had any sexual experience." He was extremely sensitive, shy, rather seclusive, and he had worried somewhat about his studies. During vacation he became restless and sleepless, began to express queer ideas such as that he thought everyone in the world knew what was in his mind, that there was a conspiracy to keep this knowledge secret. He began to express grandiose ideas, claimed that he was the Prince of Wales, a Greek god.

Admitted to the hospital, the patient was somewhat tense and over-active but was very coöperative when interviewed. He expressed the above ideas, claimed that he was various important persons and that he was merely masquerading under his ordinary name. At the same time he had some insight into the absurdity of these claims. People had been following him around for some months and they read his mind by means of mental telepathy. Occasionally he heard his own thoughts repeated. In a few days the patient ceased to parade his abnormal ideas and was anxious to return to his studies. For a few weeks he was able to get along in a doctor's house but then he became moody, left the doctor's house, and made a futile attempt to sail for England. On return to the hospital he explained that he wanted to get away from America as everybody here believed that he was insane. He talked in a quiet and complacent manner, did not at first admit any hallucinatory or delusional trends. He seemed to have no insight into the absurdity or aimless nature of his recent behavior. For over a month the patient made no reference to grandiose ideas but accepted the routine of a ward patient. At the end of this period he again made grandiose claims, said that he was a duke and felt that he and another patient should go and visit the Prince of Wales. He felt that the other patients were criminals and were trying to tack some crime on him, such as murder. Although he made these statements, the patient as before had a certain degree of insight into their abnormal nature; he said that he picked them out of the air. He admitted that these ideas had never left him although he had at times recognized them as absurd. A month later the patient continued to claim royal descent and refused to accept his father as such. One year later the patient was still in a mental hospital claiming that he was the Prince of Wales; he heard people repeating his thoughts. He was transferred to another state and two years later continued to be an inmate of a state hospital.

The above cases show how in one type of mental disorder delusional elements play an adaptive rôle, and how by means of the wish-fulfilling function of thought the individual attains a certain satisfaction although at the price of a serious surrender of the social rôle.

Group III (b)

*Patients with a world picture which is a receptacle
for discordant components of the personality*

In a second sub-group the delusional elements
do not have the same obvious adaptive significance
as in the previous sub-group. At first sight they
seem to be merely disturbing and alien elements;
their presence seems to entail not only loss of contact with one's fellows but strife and embitterment.
The nature of the inner difficulties of the patient,
the distorted view of the outside world and of
his fellows which is the attempted solution of his
problem, raise a barrier between the patient and
the physician. Detailed analysis of the steps in the
development of the psychosis and a convincing
demonstration of the significance of the symptoms
in the individual case are rarely possible. A
further difficulty is presented in many of these
cases by the form of the patient's utterances; concepts may be less precise, statements not take the
usual propositional form, the standard verbal
symbols be inadequate, new words be coined. Even
making allowance for the difficulty of the idiom
the patient's picture of the outside world cannot
be formulated as corresponding to the conscious
or unconscious wishes of the individual in the same

direct way as in the previous sub-group. The picture, however, except insofar as it may contain elements due to a non-adaptive disturbance of impersonal origin, is to be understood as the world seen through the medium of the patient's personality. The various items in the picture can often be traced to repressed factors and to unconscious elaboration. The symptoms form part of an adaptive process; the patient, unable to eliminate disturbing factors in the personality, has displaced them on to the outer world. If hostility and anger and jealousy and hate and perverse lust will thrust up their heads, at least the patient through the alchemy of thought can see the trouble in the outer world and not in himself. In this type of reaction we deal not with phantasy supplying a deficit, but with the successful rejection of responsibility for disturbing elements in the personality which cannot be altogether eliminated or ignored. These elements may have various sources. They may be deeply rooted perverse tendencies of the individual, which are tabooed and have to be repressed. They may be disturbing memories or immature tendencies which have retained an undue vitality; they may be personal trends of hate or jealousy which conflict with self-respect. The elaborate discussion of the Schreber case by Freud

is an outstanding contribution to our knowledge
of the mechanisms involved in such cases.

The following brief histories illustrate the
clinical material of this group.

Martin N., twenty-six, a laborer, had since the
age of ten been brought up by his mother, deserted
by her husband. Jealous of his younger brother he
was an irritable, seclusive boy, with no friends, no
interest in girls; a poor scholar. At the age of
twenty-five he showed a change of personality; he
became antagonistic to and critical of his mother,
abrupt in dealing with other people. After resign-
ing or losing his job he became depressed, uttered
strange ideas. He claimed that a gang had been
persecuting him, they had broken into his house
and raped his mother and threatened to kill him;
his mother was in league with these men, had given
one the deed to the house, had turned against the
patient. During spells of excitement he threatened
to kill himself and to murder his mother and
brother.

In this young man brought up in close dependence on the mother, inferior in studies and social
adaptation, with no wholesome contact with the
other sex, the dramatic external happenings which

he sees in the outside world seem closely related
to internal dangers and repressed factors.

The following patient also sees in the outside
world, as objective, elements which to the de-
tached observer seem to represent crude instinctive desires and ruminations, not recognized by
nor acceptable to the patient.

Nathan O., twenty-nine, son of an aggressive
and dominating mother, a model boy, interested in
church affairs, had accepted the fiancée chosen by
his mother. At the age of twenty-six he broke off
the engagement after a display of jealousy elicited
by a trifling incident. He gave up work, and after
several months he lost interest in his old recreations, became seclusive, stayed at home. He was
admitted to the hospital at the age of twenty-nine
after a curious incident in which he claimed that
he was fighting snakes in his mattress; he had also
received messages from his pillow. In the hospital
he claimed that people on the streets talked about
him; he was a walking aerial through which Scotland Yard talked; Scotland Yard had been after
him because he had illusions. Voices gave him
grandiose titles, urged him towards perverse
sexual activities with a high church dignitary,

talked freely of excreta. He saw a snake with
fangs which came out while he was at stool, he had
an "optical illusion of a large scratch in the eye
and bleeding." He was accused of shooting his
mother; she was connected with the police department; perhaps she was his stepmother.

Oscar P., a young man of twenty-three, as a
child had been teased on account of clumsiness,
probably due to infantile paralysis; he was shy,
disliked dirty stories. A dull scholar, he did not
finish high school, took a job for a year, but found
his fellow-workers crude and uncongenial; he
withdrew to his father's farm. He now showed
eccentric behavior, thought that the neighbors
were laughing at him. He thought much about his
sister's virtue and the danger of incestuous relations. The topic of insanity, chiefly in relation to
others, also preoccupied him; he asked if he were
going insane, thought that he had made a neighbor
insane, that his father was insane. He carried on
conversations with imaginary voices. He felt that
psychiatrists at a distance could read the magazine
which he was reading. In the hospital the patient
discussed his views, which were rather difficult to
follow; he was rather restless, suspicious, afraid
that he might be shot. After two years in mental

hospitals he was able to return to his father's farm, and during the following year gave no evidence of hallucinations or delusions. In this case the topics which stand out prominently in the patient's picture of the outside world are incest and insanity.

In the following case as in many others the alien elements in the world picture are of more obscure origin; they neither represent the fulfilment of obvious wishes nor is their relation to unacceptable trends always easy to demonstrate.

Paul M. was difficult as a boy, quarrelsome at school and at home, with few friends; at adolescence he left home in a rather stormy way, insisted on earning his own living, had many jobs, was too self-assertive and argumentative. About the age of twenty-one out of a clear sky he began to express odd ideas. He visited an old schoolmate, Elizabeth, claimed she was not the original Elizabeth, said that she had a hare-lip (false); he said that he was a Siamese twin of Elizabeth. He claimed telepathic power, refused to accept the death of an aviator friend. During the following year he continued to maintain a rather disturbing interest in Elizabeth; he finally made an unsuccessful suicidal attempt. After a period of treatment in a mental hospital he was able to resume life outside and for at least the following year supported himself by salesmanship.

Unacceptable trends may be admitted by the individual but responsibility for them may be projected on the environment; the patient sees the trends as imposed from without, not as the expression of forces from within.

Queena R., a bright but irresponsible stenographer, had lived a promiscuous life without compunction; according to her code sexual intercourse even without any social sanction was natural and normal. For some years she had shown a suspicious and resentful attitude towards her superiors, spread false stories about them. At the age of twenty-eight she gave way to an urge to resume her childhood masturbation. She felt that this was unnatural; she claimed that someone was putting this idea in her head, that in order to cause these undesirable thoughts people were concentrating on her. After a brief period of treatment in the hospital the patient returned to work and during the following five years continued to live in the community, at times suspicious and accusatory, at other times free from morbid ideas.

In the following case a similar morbid picture of the world was of rather brief duration and occurred in a person of apparently stable personality.

Rita S., thirty-six, clerk, had had a placid and uneventful career. She was a pleasant, amiable, colorless, unromantic woman; I.Q. 107. She said that she had never cared for any man; nothing was known of any friendship with the other sex. Out of a clear sky she complained that fellow-workers talked about her, made trouble for her, asked a policeman to arrest her. People in automobiles said "we'll get you yet"; a gang was after her; wires were tapped, her food poisoned. Voices whispered threats, called her a street-walker, said she was pregnant; she thought the scream of a patient was that of her sister being murdered. After these ideas had lasted for a month she was admitted to the hospital; there the symptoms began to subside after three days. She had complained of fatigue previous to admission; in the hospital there was for one day nausea and headache, but physical examination failed to throw light on the condition. The patient left the hospital within two weeks and during the following five years there had been no recurrence of symptoms.

Samuel T., twenty-two, a shipping clerk, the youngest boy in a family of seven, had been somewhat pampered by the family. He made a good record at school, then worked efficiently in an industrial establishment, spent his evenings studying for a profession. He had shown no unusual traits of character, had many friends, was not particularly interested in the other sex, was said to be introspective. After a theft in his establishment, in regard to which no one suspected him in the least, he began to talk of detectives being after him, he became sleepless, finally made a suicidal attempt by drowning. In the hospital he was pleasant and coöperative, had a good memory and grasp of general information. He discussed freely his recent experiences. He had felt that he was under suspicion owing to the loss of packages from his establishment. Suggestions had been made that his brother had not died honorably in the World War but had been a traitor; he himself, therefore, ought to end his own life and therefore he attempted suicide. For ten years he had been the subject of some scientific experiment; in the hospital he was both the subject of an experiment and was experimenting himself. He felt responsible for the condition of the patients. In the course of his stay in the hospital the patient had many ruminations about the sex topic and his mother. He thought that a nurse was pregnant, he identified her as his mother; he felt that he would have to be born again and to go through the various stages of infancy. The patient was in good physical health. He had an undescended right testicle with a slight right inguinal hernia which caused him no trouble.

In this distorted picture of the outside world one sees not only the diffuse influence of a feeling of guilt but also the presence of specific factors derived from unacceptable sexual trends.

Group III (c)

Patients with an accusatory world picture

In a third sub-group the patient's formulation of the outside world is distorted through the pervasive influence of a dominant emotion. While in the compulsive neurosis the underlying emotion causes compensatory behavior or mental gymnastics, in the present type of reaction the result is a distortion of the outside world.

Theresa U., teacher, at the age of thirty-three thought that her legs were swollen, and attributed this to masturbation. She now observed that boys would stare at her and burst out laughing, thus showing that they knew her secret. A neutral advertisement of canary birds was taken as a suggestion that she had carried on abnormal sex practices. At night she heard voices in the street, whistling and shouting; these happenings had reference to her. Three years later she maintained that everyone knew of her sex practices; she claimed that she was broadcasting, i.e., people could read her mind. A minor compensatory belief was her claim in the hospital that patients acted for her benefit. The sex life of the patient had not been smooth; it included a passive sexual experience at fourteen, ensuing masturbation at first without compunction but later with a conviction of its dread consequences, emotional turmoil over her father's remarriage, followed by a homosexual liaison with a continuing feeling of guilt.

In the following case there was the rather sudden development of a picture of the world as a censorious and all-seeing authority.

Ulysses V., a clerk, twenty-two years of age, had been a model child, an honor student at school, efficient in business. He was shy, seclusive, had few friends, attended church regularly. Without much warning he began to talk of people looking at him,

laughing at him, talking about him. He felt that
he was going insane, gave up his job "because he
could not stand the notoriety." In the hospital he
told the physicians that he was the center of interest for the whole world, that he was accused of
being immoral, a sadist; his actions were broad-
cast. He claimed that the accusations were justi-
fied inasmuch as he had stolen, lied, fornicated.
He realized that his mind was upset, he had wired
his father of his "severe mental breakdown." He
attributed his upset condition to masturbation.
The patient had been brought up in an atmosphere of severe sex repression at home; he had
indulged in excessive masturbation; the mental attack came on after a period of sexual indulgence.
After admission to the hospital he became steadily
more convinced that his ideas were imaginary,
within two months was practically well and during
the following four years had shown no relapse.

A similar abrupt onset of ideas of reference on
the basis of a sense of guilt over continuing masturbation, with rapid recovery, was seen in the following case.

Vincent W., seventeen, was a silent, sullen, solitary boy in an unhappy home with a shiftless

father and an unstable stepmother. He suddenly claimed that people were tooting horns at him, talking about him, laughing at him; he interpreted casual remarks as having reference to him. After two or three weeks he was admitted to the hospital. In the hospital he expressed these morbid ideas; he also told of having masturbated for one year previous to admission and of having recently been frightened by a priest with the threat of Hell. The patient after discussion with the physician readily gave up his misinterpretations, left the hospital apparently well after nine days, and during the following year there was no recurrence of symptoms.

One must recognize that many symptoms are determined in a complex way and express combined and conflicting attitudes and emotions. What is apparently dreaded by the patient may have its own fascination; what appears to be quite distasteful may have a certain charm. Accusations of guilt may partake of the nature of a compliment; many a conventional person is flattered by the suggestion of his having sown wild oats or being something of a dare-devil.

Vera X., thirty-nine, had ideas of reference similar to those of the previous patient; in the apparently distasteful or hostile attentions of others, while a feeling of guilt no doubt played a rôle, underlying wishes also seemed to betray themselves. Rather dull at school, she had been a bright sociable young woman. From seventeen to thirty-three she masturbated and, according to her statement, without compunction. At thirty-seven there was a sexual indiscretion; shortly after this a thyroidectomy. During convalescence from this operation she complained of bodily odor, was seclusive, embarrassed in her brother's presence; she felt that everyone, especially men, were conscious of the odor. She gave up her job. She continued to notice that people smiled at her in a knowing way, plain-clothes men followed her, thought she was a street-walker; men followed her either with evil intentions or representing the police. She claimed that she was about to have a baby as the result of her indiscretion two years previously. The patient stated that she had psychic powers.

In Walter Y., a lad of seventeen, the same idea of body odor seemed to represent merely the feeling of taint or guilt and not to be fostered or exploited by any latent wishes. At the age of fifteen the boy was considerably disturbed by the erotic conversation and behavior of fellow-workers.

At sixteen he thought that his father had discovered him masturbating; from this time he felt
that people avoided him on account of his body
odor. He therefore bathed unusually frequently,
was seclusive, walked on the street with his head
bowed down in order to avoid recognition. During
three months' stay in the hospital he made some
improvement. A more dramatic and obvious
change was seen after his visit to a miracle man
who had previously cured his mother and who
made use of a potent "Rosy-Cross." The patient
became well enough to act as chauffeur for the
miracle man and to be a support to the latter when
the miracle man was admitted to the psychopathic
department of a general hospital. There had apparently been no return of symptoms for three
years after leaving the hospital.

I am afraid that I have stirred too many crude
facts into the general presentation of our topic
and that there may seem to be a dearth of general
ideas. A general discussion of the schizophrenic
field is, however, apt to become verbal and scho-
lastic unless there is clearly in evidence the concrete material upon which the discussion is based.
The discussion may be summarized as follows:

In the large group of the schizophrenic psychoses intensive research into isolated processes should not cause neglect of the broader features of the symptomatology and course of the psychosis, in other words, of the drama presented by the individual life.

In some cases the drama of the psychosis is one of turmoil and unrest, without even a transitory equilibrium, and with an outcome difficult to foresee. In other cases there is less turmoil, but the individual in the face of life difficulties gropes for an adaptation by withdrawal from contact with the outer world, or by mobilizing the resources of his thought processes; this kind of adaptation is but a faulty solution for the life problem, it may supply only a temporary resting place, it is accepted at the price of estrangement from one's fellows and of the surrender of one's social rôle.

In reviewing different types of life-history, emphasis has been laid on this or that mental mechanism or mode of reaction. None of these mechanisms nor type of reaction is a specific characteristic of any mental disorder; they are general characteristics of the human personality, more highly developed, it is true, in some individuals than in others.

The discussion has emphasized the desirability of looking on the psychosis as merely one phase of the patient's adaptation to his life situation, and of paying due attention to this background in the intensive investigation of specific symptoms and possible causes. Physiological, biochemical, and histopathological investigations are of importance but the results have to be evaluated in the setting of the personality, of the human needs of the patient, of the demands made upon him by the environment.

III

OUR KINSHIP WITH
THE SCHIZOPHRENIC

THE various points of view and the various methods of those working in the field of mental disorders were summarily reviewed in our first lecture. In the second lecture we entered the field of the schizophrenic psychoses, those serious mental disorders which fill our mental hospitals and raise so many and such diverse issues. A summary review of our material indicated that, no matter whether an underlying impersonal process be present or not, the behavior and outlook of the patient seem in part to be the expression of underlying needs of the personality and of an attempt at adaptation to the demands and the deficiencies of the life situation. With a schizophrenic patient the psychiatrist is dealing with more than a disease, he is dealing with a fragment of an individual destiny. A few types of reaction were briefly discussed. In many cases there seemed to be mere conflict and turmoil; in other cases restriction of interest and lack of response were the outstanding features; in a third group a delusional picture of the outside world dominated the clinical picture.

In this third lecture I should like to return to the problems of the schizophrenic psychoses in order to discuss some general principles and some particular symptoms, to illustrate how the general trends of psychiatry outlined in the first lecture converge upon the particular problems of the second lecture.

The psychosis reveals much about the personality of the patient, it throws light on the stability of its integration, on basic patterns of reaction, on the special component forces involved in its dynamic equilibrium. Without the critical revealing episode of the psychosis we should often have little measure of the degree of integration or cohesiveness of the personality, little indication of the underlying patterns of reaction, no insight into the complexity of the component forces. It is true that what is revealed is often no simple factor but complex qualities requiring further analysis; we have much to learn about the vulnerability of the individual, the significance of the patterns of reaction, the determinants of the component forces.

In face of the schizophrenic patient, as of many an hysterical patient, the baffled observer asks him-

self in perplexity: How can anyone make such perplexing utterances, behave in such a preposterous
way, unless either possessed by a devil or by a
disease? Having denied the devil, must we accept
the disease? In Salem, in 1692, the weird utterances and bizarre behavior of some young women,
which led to the death of nineteen innocent people
as witches, were attributed to the presence of evil
spirits; today their behavior would be described in
terms of symptoms, and the underlying disorder
would receive a Greek name. While the Greek
term hysteria may be useful for the orderly arrangement of our clinical material, it need not
cramp our thought, and we can understand these
preposterous Salem experiences in terms of human
nature and culture, in terms of primitive thought
and prevalent beliefs, in terms of such human
traits as credulity, phantasy, desire for notoriety,
ignorance, spite. The behavior of these young
women was not to be understood as the manifestation of a disease, of an underlying impersonal
process; its development from previously conventional behavior in each single case could no doubt
have been traced step by step in the light of the
individual personality, the past experiences, the
actual situation, the cultural atmosphere.

The step by step transition from the behavior

of the sane individual as conventionally conceived to the schizophrenic clinical picture is more difficult to trace, and to some the transition may seem to involve a complete discontinuity, attributed to an underlying disease process. The continuous transition from the behavior of the sane individual more adequately conceived, with his complex organization, his organic urges, primitive attitudes, persistent childhood desires and attitudes and phantasies, his egoistic demands, sexual needs, and social cravings, to the schizophrenic psychosis, may not be impossible to follow. Before maintaining that such a continuous transition without the intervention of a disease process is *impossible,* we do well first to ascertain whether it is *actual,* whether it is a fact at least in some cases, and to what extent this fact aids in the general interpretation of these disorders. Then may come the next question: How can we fit these data into our psychology, harmonize them with our systematic views on human thought and behavior? The latter task may be difficult; the system may have to be remodelled to accept the new data.

The natives of a tropical climate might protest against the suggestion that water when cooled below 4° actually expands and finally becomes solid in virtue of its own intrinsic qualities; they might argue that it could not behave so, unless be-witched or suffering from some disease. In the field of human behavior, also, it may be difficult to understand *how* certain things happen. The phe-nomena may conflict with conventional formula-tions. If they do conflict then it is not the facts but the formulations that must be rejected; the data must be woven into the organized body of our knowledge.

One may take as an example the stuporous reac-tion, in which the individual withdraws interest from or loses interest in the outside world. This may have to be looked on as one mode of reaction of the human personality, a quality of the organ-ism as a whole, a quality not created by conditions of disease, but revealed by one of nature's experi-ments. Stupor and ice may have to be considered as qualities of nature, not created by an alien power but revealed by special conditions; in the one case by climatic conditions, in the other case by the winter of man's discontent.

If this reaction has to be looked on as an innate characteristic of the human personality, then one would look for its occurrence in milder as well as in more severe forms, in simpler as well as in more complex settings. We are as a matter of fact familiar with this reaction in conditions of mental distress. A good example is furnished in the life of Liszt. At seventeen the love affair in which his romantic and sensitive nature was profoundly engaged was abruptly and frigidly terminated by the father of his pupil. Liszt's first reaction was to endeavor to enter holy orders, but his confessor, a lover of music, refused to grant his request. Liszt withdrew within himself, took to his bed where he spent weeks with closed shutters, and for eighteen months it was hardly possible to extract a word from him. In the last lecture I referred briefly to a case of still more profound stupor after the abrupt and tactless termination of a love affair.

In other individuals this same type of reaction may be brought into play under conditions of less profound distress but in response to wounded pride, perhaps even with some exploitation of the dramatic possibilities in the situation. Rousseau in his *Confessions* gives us an interesting picture of such an episode. His friend, Grimm, had been rejected by an actress to whom he had paid court: "He fell suddenly into the strangest sickness that one has perhaps ever heard of. He passed his days and nights in a continual lethargy, the eyes open, the pulse good, but without speaking, without eating, without budging, appearing sometimes to hear, never answering, not even making a sign; and for the rest without agitation, without pain, without fever and remaining there as if dead. ... The patient remained several days immobile, without taking bouillon or anything else save some preserved cherries. ... One fine day he rose, dressed himself and resumed his ordinary course of life, without ever speaking to me nor as far as I know to anyone of this singular lethargy."

While we may be entitled to look upon the stuporous reaction as indicating a fundamental quality of the individual's personality, the detailed nature of this pattern of reaction, as of other more familiar biological reactions such as fear and depression, deserves further investigation. In the individual case the factors which have thrown this mechanism into action require careful scrutiny and the physician must attribute their respective rôles to bodily factors, internal tensions, external situations. To one individual this reaction, just as the hysterical reaction, may be much more easily available than to another.

The stuporous reaction has to be seen on a broad background. The human mind cannot assimilate everything; cataclysms of nature, bereavement or catastrophic change of fortune, may precipitate not fear nor depression, but a dull, un-

comprehending, unresponsive condition. Too
dread an experience may not be assimilated nor
woven into the continuum of memory. Schopenhauer emphasized this a century before Freud, although in terms somewhat different from those of
the clinician: "In the resistance of the will against
allowing what is distasteful to come into the il-
lumination of the intellect, lies the place where
insanity can break into the mind. Each distasteful
new occurrence must be assimilated by the intellect, that is, receive a place in the system of those
truths which are related to our will and its interest
even if it may have squeezed out some more grati-
fying element. As soon as this has happened it is
already much less painful. But this operation itself
is often very painful, proceeds only slowly and
with resistance. In the meantime mental health
can only exist in so far as this operation is each
time really completed. If, on the other hand, in
an individual case the resistance and antagonism
of the will to the reception of some information
reaches the degree that that operation cannot be
clearly carried out, if then certain occurrences or
incidents are repressed from the intellect, because
the will cannot bear their contemplation, if then
on account of the necessity for continuity the ensuing gap is filled up according to the pleasure

of the individual, then is insanity there, for intellect has given up its nature to please the will. The individual imagines what is not, but the insanity which arises in this way becomes the Lethe of intolerable pains." In another place the philosopher states the same principle more briefly: "This painful acceptance of distasteful and stubborn facts, against which the individual protests and offers resistance may be beyond the endowment of the individual. The tortured spirit tears, so to speak, the thread of memory, fills the gaps with fictions and takes flight from the pain which goes beyond its strength, in insanity."

Schopenhauer calls attention to the fact that memory may fail to record what cannot be borne, and Liszt illustrates the individual in distress actually withdrawing from the world. These considerations may be relevant in greater or less degree to the analysis of several patients discussed in the second lecture (especially Group II (b)), but are by no means put forward as doing justice to the complexity and variety of the factors involved in these cases.

While the stuporous reaction may not be so obviously adaptive as the simple emotional reactions of fear and rage, with their complicated mobilization of the physiological systems, it is per-

haps more easy to attribute an adaptive value to
it than to the more familiar reaction of depression.
Stupor is less obviously adaptive than the reactions of the psychoneuroses, it is more obviously
so than the affective type of reaction. In the case
of apathy and lack of response, of poor assimila-
tion, of forgetfulness in the face of trying experiences, the reaction protects the personality from
the invasion of elements which it is unable to
assimilate. The reaction may reveal a special
quality of the organism in the same way as an
hysterical, compulsive, or affective reaction.

General psychology based on the study of the
so-called normal individual may not offer to the
psychiatrist much help in the understanding of
such problems as those of the stuporous patient;
on the other hand the psychiatrist by the study
of these patients may bring to general psychology
an invaluable experimental material, throwing
light on the variety of individual temperaments
as well as on detailed psychological mechanisms.

The details of the varied schizophrenic clinical
pictures present many special problems which are
not to be easily disposed of by any general
formula. Akinetic and hyperkinetic symptoms require much further study. The similarity of motor
symptoms in schizophrenic patients to post-

encephalitic syndromes and to the behavior of
bulbocapninized animals may be superficial, and
premature identification is to be avoided. It is not
enough to resolve the motor phenomena into component neurophysiological elements: one must
consider their possible rôle as elements in more
complex patterns. Such a pattern may have a kinship with the death-feint of animals, the reaction
of primitive man to magic, the motor symptoms
in hypnosis, the ecstasies of the saints, the postures
of the fakir on the banks of the Ganges. This
applies not only to postures but also to special
movements and gestures. The situation is well
illustrated by Jung's patient who for decades had
lain in bed reacting to nothing, speaking to
nobody, with fixed posture, but making peculiar
rubbing movements with her hands, the thumb and
index finger of her right hand held together as in
sewing. Such a phenomenon could, of course, be
thought of in purely neurological terms, but limitation to these terms and concepts would certainly
have failed to make the situation as clear as the
review of the total situation. Years before the
repetitive movements had deteriorated into their
apparently meaningless form, the pattern had been
much clearer. The movements had been those of
the shoemaker as he sews his shoes. When the

patient had entered the hospital thirty-five years previously it had been after a love affair which had come to nothing; her lover had been a shoemaker. The repetitive movements, therefore, were no mere meaningless neurological activities, they were the symbolic expression, maintained for thirty-five years, of what had been the culminating experience in the life of this woman.

So the recurrent utterances "I do, I do," of a woman of thirty-eight would have been equally unintelligible unless taken in the setting of the total situation. After brooding over the loss of her sweetheart for many years she finally claimed that she was married to him, at the same time carrying out marriage rites, lighting candles and repeating "I do, I do."

In religious ritual, postures, gestures and stereotyped procedures play a familiar rôle: to the uninitiated they are without significance, aimless, and without value; to the initiated they may have little adaptive significance, but they have emotional value derived from the traditional ritual and all that it means to them. To the individual who has studied the history of the ritual the movements and procedures are seen to be the somewhat disguised or modified residuals of procedures which were once definitely adaptive and which at an earlier cultural period had played an important rôle in the adaptation of the tribe to the mysterious forces by which it was surrounded.

The schizophrenic may have personal needs which are not satisfied by the standard procedures and beliefs of his fellows. He works out his own creed and constructs his own ritual. To the uninitiated and the unsympathetic this ritual may appear a meaningless disorder, the product of diseased neurones, the symptoms of an underlying disease. Catatonia in some cases may have to be studied not as a disease but as a religion is studied; it may represent the attempted adaptation of human nature to its special inner needs and external demands. This individual adaptation, however, is a religion to which there is only one adherent, and in an intolerant community the only place for worship available may be within the walls of the mental hospital.

Hyperkinetic and akinetic phenomena are recognized and accepted elements in many religious settings; they may take the form of the somewhat disorganized and exuberant manifestations of the camp meeting, or they may have a more definite pattern peculiar to the special sect. No matter how eccentric the motor manifestations of our patients may be, the clinical picture cannot be adequately evaluated unless one keeps in mind these broader determinants of motor reactions as well as the impersonal neurological mechanisms.

Occasionally a person of unusual endowment manages to combine his personal ritual and beliefs with the maintenance of sound personal relations, and through his prestige may even impose upon others his own creed and thus organize a group as did Comte with his worship of Clotilde de Vaux. In the study of our patients it is well to remember the behavior of this man of distinguished intellect and great force of character. He erected the chair in which his dead friend Clotilde had sat into a domestic altar. Three times a day he went through prolonged religious exercises in her honor. He repeated numbers with their mystical significance. He had stereotyped and complicated phrases of adoration to the departed beloved. His whole philosophical system was remoulded in order to do justice to this new element in his life. Some may at once consider such procedures and associated beliefs as indicating the presence of some underlying disease. Comte already had had a well-marked attack of insanity at the age of twenty-eight, an attack characterized by great turmoil and diagnosed by Esquirol himself as mania. This earlier attack, at a period when he was under great emotional and intellectual stress, gives some insight into the vulnerability or lack of sound integration of his personality, and shows that there were limits to the tension which he could support. The repressed forces in that early attack broke through in a fragmentary and disintegrated manner. The same individual in his later years managed to integrate these forces into a mode of life and a philosophical system which did not conflict with social requirements and which even permitted the development of a new religion, the positivist religion, to which many individuals of merit subscribed.

Religious beliefs, like other biological manifestations, are subject to the selective action of the environment. Some persist while others although more logical in form and sound in structure may fall by the wayside. The structure of religious belief may be essentially the same, whether it be the belief of a single individual, of a small sect, or of a large and influential church.

From the point of view of private ritual and behavior one may also refer to Father Doyle with his self-flagellation even with razor blades, his asceticism and his great emphasis on repetitive exclamations, so that even when on duty at the front in war time he managed, according to his reckoning, to raise the daily number of brief aspirations or ejaculatory prayers to one hundred thousand. This private ritual of Father Doyle took place in the setting of a life of professional efficiency and of high social value, in intimate contact with his fellowmen.

Reference has been made to Comte and to Father Doyle to show how individuals of great value may deal with the total problem of life, and how special symptoms which we are apt to associate exclusively with clinical pictures may also play a rôle in the setting of an efficient life. The symptoms are to be understood in the light of an analysis which includes not only the bodily functions but the individual personality and the cultural beliefs in which the individual is steeped. One might devote some time to a study of even simpler functions and their anomalies in the setting of the abnormal and of the normal life. Personal care and regard for decency are among the everyday problems of those caring for mental patients. Before attributing the dilapidated behavior of all untidy patients to impersonal processes one has to keep in mind the fact that in people of high spiritual level there have also been interesting manifestations in this sphere, and the odor of sanctity, symbolic of spiritual value, may have had very humble sources.

The same general point of view applies to that other group of cases (Group III), in which behavior is not primarily so much involved but where delusions dominate the clinical picture, the individual having mobilized the thought processes to elaborate a symbolic picture of the world which makes the internal equilibrium of the patient more satisfactory.

One meets here the same problem as in cases of bizarre and dilapidated behavior, the difficulty of seeing the psychological steps which intervene between normal mentality as conventionally understood and the mentality which constructs a hopelessly inconsistent and phantastic picture of the outside world and presents it to us in speech of obscure and novel character. It may be intelligible to us that a patient should see the world in the light of his desires and should be blind to the disagreeable. It requires more effort to understand the phantastic ideas which deal with mysterious forces in the universe and with various forms of control of the patient's thoughts, to understand the contradictory and inconsistent statements as to identity, the bizarre claims as to bodily structures and processes. Along with visions and

voices of familiar type, such as those connected
with religious and other overt preoccupations, one
meets fragmentary hallucinatory experiences which
at first sight seem to have no connection with
known forces or elements in the patient's personality. Here, too, the alternative of devil or
disease is the simple formulation. Before accept-
ing the hypothesis of impersonal disease, however,
one again reviews the fullness of human nature,
the underlying atavistic beliefs, the persistent
childhood formulations, repressed memories associated with guilt and fear, repressed tendencies of
the appetites and the affections. One does justice
to the rôle of repression, projection, symbolism.
With the human personality understood in terms
of the above component forces the development
of even a phantastic picture of the outside world
may become in large part intelligible, may perhaps not require the introduction of any extraneous
factor of disease. Dream analysis has shown how,
when the personality in sleep temporarily gives
up the effort of integrative control and of adaptation to the demands of a real world, the strangest
products develop. In the dream, a familiar recurrent phenomenon, we have a phantastic, non-
adaptive mental product. In the psychosis as in
sleep the adaptive effort may be reduced or com-

pletely abandoned, and the realistic function of thought no longer have authority. With the abandonment of interest in the real world, and of the controlling influence of adaptation to the real world with its social values, the critical supervision of words, concepts, syntax, logic is also relaxed. The rigid control of these factors is necessary for mutual communication in the real world, for observing precisely and anticipating the sequence of events in the real world, for taking the necessary practical steps in one's efforts to carry on activity in the real world. The concepts, propositional forms and logical criteria, so important in the real world, are of little importance to him who has abandoned the task of getting satisfaction from the real world and for whom the real world has become rather shadowy, a theatre or a mere past existence before the *Weltuntergang*. To such an individual his own inner life and tendencies dominate the total experience and fill up the gap left by the disappearance of the solid reality. The happenings within his own experience are now reality, conflicts which he feels within himself are referred to as cosmic or mundane conflicts; he may grope around in an effort to specify this general conflict, it is a conflict between East and West, between Jew and Gentile, between

Protestant and Catholic. He not only sees general conflicts of this nature, but feels involved in magical forces, is subject to strange hostile influences formulated in terms of telepathy, hypnotism and control in general. In this world of chaos the various factors may take on hallucinatory vividness, perhaps dependent on the special imagery of the individual, and voices and visions diversify the clinical picture. The phantastic picture, however, when the totality of the human personality is considered, is not so unintelligible as at first appears. One not only sees where many of the individual factors come from, but one learns much about the dynamics of the human personality. One may trace to its inception the disturbance of the equilibrium and follow the various steps in the disturbance. The study of these experiments of nature makes an important contribution to general psychology and throws light upon the complexity of the thought processes.

As with regard to stupor and motor manifestations, so here too one considers in what other settings analogous reactions occur, what conditions exist where one meets phantastic pictures of the outside world and the formulation of the individual's views in non-logical utterances with newformed words and curiously elusive concepts.

Reference has been made to the familiar phenomenon of the dream, beneath the phantastic structure of which Freud taught us to see at work the profound forces of human nature. The curious verbal expressions which occur in dreams had already for many years been carefully observed by Kraepelin.

As to the abnormal forms of expression of our patients, which are as perplexing as the content of the phantastic world picture which they put before us, we do well to remember that even in normal waking life important communications are not always made in direct and logical form. It may be indiscreet to say things directly, and the statement actually made may have little significance if the words be given their usual connotation, while it indicates sufficiently to the initiated the important fact thus symbolized. The ordinary verbal symbols may not be adequate to express an unusual experience. Through carelessness or in jest the individual may use a symbol not in current use, such as the term "volumptuous." In political cartoons one has a good example of how a very important meaning and evaluation may be expressed in a form which, taken at its face value, is hopelessly absurd and incongruous. What separates the cartoon from the schizophrenic production is that the former remains a means of social communication, it takes cognizance of recognized symbols, it keeps within control the purely individual and only puts forth that which can be interpreted by one's fellows. In the schizophrenic the need for such control is gone. The control exercised by the judgment of others and by the circumstances of the real situation is no longer in effect or only partially so; in his images and in his verbal and pictorial products he can give complete scope to the play of his own egoistic tendencies, conscious and subconscious.

Human expression is not always limited to communications dealing with mere matter-of-fact and practical judgment. The expressions of the poet may deal with other values and may express different needs, and here the language differs from that of realistic, objective presentation. Concepts, words, and arrangement of words are much more fluid. It may not be possible to translate the exact significance of the poet's expression into terms of prose, yet we feel that the poetical expression has great value, a value which perhaps could not have been rendered in prose form by means of the ordinary concepts and words and formal propositions. The poet does not expect us to take his words and phrases in the same sense in which we

take them in a catalogue. A brother poet refers to
Shelley as "gold-dusty from tumbling among the
stars," and we feel the adequacy of the description. In Elizabethan times there was a spring-like
joy in the fresh words of the language; the
Euphuists took a special delight in their manip-
ulation. Shakespeare in the richness of his
imagination found the existing supply of words
inadequate and had to coin new symbols to do
justice to the treasures of his mind. In doing so
he had in mind his fellows; he not only found a
more adequate means of self-expression but he
endowed his fellows with a much richer language.

Pearsall Smith says of the time of Shakespeare:
"In that age of complete linguistic freedom and
experimental gusto the making of words became
the sport of sports among the young intellectuals
of fashion. How they created and coined and
fantasticated them to please their fancy, made
them ring and sing and rhyme together without a
thought whether reason had any hand in the
matter!" Smith refers to some writers as "word-
eccentrics" and talks of Spenser making "for himself a precious form of speech for his private use."

The schizophrenic, out of touch with his fellows, has little thought for whether his new-coined
word will communicate anything to them or

whether it will be to them an additional tool. It is for him a means of personal expression and this is its whole purpose.

In some poetry the conventional conceptual significance of the word seems to play a vanishing rôle; the word or its component has a special meaning for the poet in view of his own psychological make-up. Thus Rimbaud claimed that he had discovered the color of the vowels. It would be of value to those who study the unusual words and forms of expression of the schizophrenic, to have some familiarity with the adventures in verbal expression of the euphuists in prose and of the imagists and symbolists and dadaists and still more modern schools in verse. In the *Jabber-wocky* we have a series of verbal symbols so similar to those of standard use and arranged in such a familiar poetical form that we get something of the elevated feeling which is conveyed to us by poetry of a more conventional type. We are somewhat in the position of the choir boy who for years had sung "twirl about ten" with the same devout feeling and with the same edification as if he had used the standard verbal symbols "world without end." The old lady who requested that the word Mesopotamia be introduced into the prayer because it did her so much good had found in that word a verbal symbol particularly appropriate to bring about a desired end of great emotional value to her. Thus Jung's patient satisfied her craving for prestige and recognition by claiming that she was *Doppelpolytechnicum* as well as "the Monopoly" and various other high-sounding things and people.

In the group of patients (Group III) in whom the distorted picture of the outside world is the outstanding feature, as in that group (Group II (b)) where motor anomalies are more prominent, even the more striking and ominous symptoms may represent modes of human reaction which are also familiar in other settings. Empirically they may be of prognostic importance but they are not unequivocal evidence of the presence of some alien impersonal process.

One of the most important factors in the schizophrenic type of reaction is the so-called dissociation between the thought processes and the feeling tone. Normally certain mental contents are accompanied by a certain affect or feeling-tone and by behavior or facial expression of a certain type. In the schizophrenic, mental content, feeling-tone, and behavior may show a certain independence or incongruity. In this incongruity do we see evidence of some new factor, some impersonal disturbance, or does it represent an already-existing quality of the individual, one mode of human reaction which can be demonstrated in other settings?

Serious situations tend normally to elicit a depressive reaction. We have seen that serious situations may be met in another way, with a dull unreceptive defensive attitude which may even ignore the occurrence or which may register it without assimilating it. There is still another way of meeting the serious issues of life, of blunting their cutting edge and taking the sting out of their attack. This is the whimsical mode of reaction by which the individual recognizes the situation but fails to be overwhelmed by it, refuses to take it at its full value, minimizes its claim, treats it as of little worth, and himself as perfectly competent to deal with it. This is not an efficient and fundamental method of dealing with serious problems but it may be one way of dealing with situations which otherwise might overwhelm us, from which we cannot escape, and for which we feel ourselves inadequate.

The ghastly tragedy of war was perhaps all the better supported by those so endowed that they could enter into the whimsical humor of Captain Bairnsfather's *The Better 'Ole* and other pictures, and treat one of the blackest pages of human folly and irrationality with a certain humorous detachment. The whimsical note in the *Prologue in Heaven*, where Mephistopheles expresses his pleasure in keeping in touch with God (*der Alte*) by occasional visits, tends to alleviate somewhat the heavy burden of the tragedy. The tragi-comedy of ordinary life might be the better supported by those who attended morality plays and early English comedy and saw how God, the devil and various other characters could discuss the serious issues of life with a certain whimsical note which relieved the grimness of the real situation. In such a presentation of life's issues the affect may not be adequate nor show the conventional relation to the mental content, but perhaps human nature through such incongruous or whimsical re-actions is better able to support the otherwise intolerable burden of life, with the overwhelming problems of evil, of pain, and death. Pearsall Smith refers to Shakespeare's clowns "with their ironic detachment like Hamlet's and their wit like his *touching melancholy with a sting of absurdity,* turning life inside out and upside down with their disintegrated phrases."

The schizophrenic is sometimes such a whimsical fellow. He deals in an apparently flippant and trivial way with major issues, but there is a great deal more true emotion present than appears on the surface. This mode of reaction may be looked upon as partly of adaptive nature and not merely as a destructive break in the machinery of the personality.

Thus as we review the schizophrenic psychoses, considering not only the broad outlines of the stuporous and delusional reactions, but also the details of behavior and of utterance, the apparent gap between the schizophrenic and the normal mentality decreases. The schizophrenic begins to appear less alien, his idiom becomes more intelligible, his behavior resolves itself into a caricature of the familiar traits of human nature.

One reason for the apparently impassable gap between the schizophrenic and ourselves has been that we in our pride refused to see human nature as it is, and when our own human nature was revealed to us by our schizophrenic fellows we disowned them as possessed by devils or made incomprehensible through disease. What kinship could there be between cultured man and Caliban?

Nature is a great laboratory, constantly undertaking experiments, trying out new combinations to form a human personality, conditioning the new individual by unusual circumstances, exposing him to novel and extreme situations. Unfortunately nature works in her own way, chooses her own time and place, does not determine her experiments according to the needs of the experimental laboratory. The experimenter must therefore bide his time till he gets from nature material relevant to his research, but when it comes it may be material of very great value and such as he cannot duplicate in his laboratory. He cannot determine the genetic endowment of an individual and trace the later evolution of the specific combination of genes; he has to take the individual as a given quantity and through a detailed genetic study and review of the individual evolution gather some data in relation to the complex problem of the influence of hereditary factors upon the individual destiny. He cannot determine experimentally variations in the original components which become blended into the later sexual cravings of the individual; he has to take the given individuals, endeavor to record at the earliest age the special manifestations of these components and trace their evolution in the setting of the individual life situation. He cannot tamper with the life of the individual to obtain the information he seeks, but the individuals he has to treat have been exposed to a great variety of tests and he may try to evaluate the reactions. He may have the opportunity of studying a young man brought up through his youth in isolation from his fellows because his mother feared his illegitimate birth might become known. He may study the effect on the personality of a young woman of having had from girlhood a serious facial disfigurement. He may study the effect on the personality of a young woman of a childhood interview with her insane mother who obscenely reviled her. He may study the effects on the adult personality of the manifold influences and experiences which touch the sex life, such as incestuous experiences in childhood with the residual secrecy, feeling of guilt and uncleanness. He has at his disposal striking experiments in the way of deprivation. He may have the opportunity of reconstructing the life history of a young woman starved from childhood of many of the requisites for normal development, brought up in early childhood by alcoholic parents, working after the age of ten as a drudge in a foster home, from the age of twenty engaged in menial work, living a life without affection or recreation or opportunities for self-expression. The influence of the prevalent beliefs in the family circle may be studied in individuals who have been brought up in a variety of superstitious or sectarian homes in which astrological, animistic, magical and crude deistic forces are part of the accepted order of things. He may have the opportunity of studying in detail how the pervading influence of a parent enters into the personality of the growing individual, and so stamps it that the development of independence, individuality and a mature attitude towards adult problems such as marriage becomes impossible. These experiments throw light on the personality and on its tasks. They serve to demonstrate the various mechanisms and types of adaptive behavior and symbolic activity, the limits of the adaptive powers, the nature and severity of adaptive failure and of personal disintegration.

The analysis of these experiments should help us to estimate the comparative importance of a variety of environmental factors. Some investigators minimize the effect of environmental influences and look upon them as more or less irrelevant to the schizophrenic disorders. They point to the fact that there was no definite increase in the schizophrenic psychoses caused by the recent war, and seem to argue that if such a major cataclysm caused few schizophrenic disorders minor domestic anomalies and social stresses can hardly be looked upon as of importance.

In war there is a direct threat to the life of the soldier. In the conflict between self-preservation and the herd instinct or group loyalty hysterical conditions developed, the familiar war-neuroses; with the development of a physical incapacity the individual was safe and self-respect was maintained.

In peace time we find the same hysterical symptoms as in war. The conflict is here, however, not between self-preservation and the herd instinct but most commonly between the biological sex urge and the herd instinct which demands from us loyalty to cultural restrictions. In the hysteria of peace as in that of war time the patient finds an evasive compromise between conflicting forces. Thus through the development of symptoms, whether in peace or in war, certain external dangers and restrictions are removed or circumvented, and the hysterical patient continues to live in the world of reality and even to exploit it.

The fact that there was no appreciable increase in the schizophrenic psychoses due to the war is perhaps irrelevant to the general question as to whether environmental factors play an important rôle in the development of the schizophrenic psychoses. There are other environmental stresses than the mere threat to life, and the question is, How does the individual personality deal with these environmental stresses and with the result-

ing internal difficulties? The review of our schizophrenic material does not suggest that the disorder
is a way of evading an external danger or of
exploiting an environment; it seems a special way
of dealing with much more subtle problems, not
with the crude dangers which threaten life but
with threats to the integrity of the personality and
to its value. In the schizophrenic psychoses external danger and the resultant fear seem to have
small part. The patient is not concerned about the
preservation of his life, but is preoccupied with
the question of personal value and with the relationship between himself and the social group.
An underlying feeling of inferiority or of guilt in
the schizophrenic is much more common than an
underlying fear, and when we come across the
apparent fear of external danger we frequently
find that this is a disguise which covers some hid-
den internal danger with its threat to the value
of the personality.

In discussing the rôle of environmental factors,
therefore, one must not forget that there are other
things that try the soul of man besides external
danger with the threat of annihilation; there are
circumstances which destroy self-confidence, which
foster a feeling of inferiority, which stifle inde-

pendence, which give rise to a feeling of guilt, of inner corruption, of impending doom.

It is on factors which touch such topics as the above that we lay emphasis when we are considering the external factors which may contribute to the development of the schizophrenic psychoses. In tracing the development of a schizophrenic psychosis we see the individual with his own special constitution, moulded by his own unique life situation, passing into his schizophrenic experience not on account of cataclysms or catastrophes, but under the joint influence of subtle pervading and continuously acting external factors and of the directing image of his inner goal.

Our summary and fragmentary review of the schizophrenic psychoses, in which we have tried to see how far one can bridge the gap between the schizophrenic and the normal with the material already at our disposal, may indicate what a wealth of material of the most varied nature, bearing upon the structure of the human personality and upon the forces that mould it, is at the disposal of the clinical psychiatrist. Jung has commented on the fact that some workers assume that to study nature one should withdraw to the laboratory and shut nature out with closed windows and doors. It may be necessary for the accurate and precise study of detailed mechanisms to isolate certain factors and to withdraw from the disturbing fullness of nature, but we must recognize that this withdrawal is a provisional procedure for specialized purposes and for refinement of analysis.

For the study of human nature it is well not to remain too closely within academic confines, but if the experiments of nature are to be utilized to supplement the precise experiments of the laboratory, they must be studied with the same clear formulation of problems, with the same degree of precision so far as the nature of the problems allows it, and with the same critical analysis and interpretation demanded in the laboratory. If it is the privilege of clinical psychiatry to have a unique material to deal with, it is also a great responsibility. The clinical psychiatrist can neither turn over this responsibility to the neurophysiologist, to the internist, nor to the psychoanalyst. He has to accept his varied material, including many cases where precise biochemical and internist studies cannot be carried out, others which do not fulfill the exacting demands of the psychoanalytic procedure, still other cases which involve the total situation to such a degree that the detailed analysis of the individual is only a small part of the total problem. He has to trace the disordered behavior and utterances of his patients to somatic status, original endowment, conditioning factors, personal equilibrium, situational stress. This exacting task includes a painstaking analysis of the family and personal history, of the complex factors involved in family and in social life. For the accurate reconstruction of the individual case one requires not only a clear formulation of the problem and an unusual expenditure of time, but skilled technical assistance.

The clinical psychiatrist, who makes his goal a conscientious reconstruction of the evolution of the individual case and utilizes to the full this experimental material, will bring to the general field of psychology a valuable material which can be derived from no other source. It is obvious that owing to the very nature of the material few individual case records will be complete, but even those records which show unavoidable gaps may furnish extremely valuable data with regard to specific topics. There are many important topics in the field of human adaptation into which clinical analysis has furnished the deepest insight.

With these demands made upon him the clinical psychiatrist must contemplate with humility the actual material which he supplies. He finds his case-histories full of gaps, the reliability of informants dubious, the chronology loose, facile interpretation instead of adequate precise observation, equivocal terms, a multiplicity of variables. The systematic collection and analysis of this invaluable psychological material, which promises to throw light on some of the major problems of human nature and of human relations, receive comparatively little support. The work too frequently has to be done under conditions which make precision and completeness unattainable. Even in the large mental hospitals where a wealth of material is available, adequate resources have still to be supplied for a systematic and thorough attack upon fundamental problems. Research in this field has, curiously enough, little of the prestige that goes with the investigation of detailed impersonal processes of which, however, it is the necessary supplement. Its lack of prestige has the unfortunate corollary of lack of funds.

In conclusion:

It has been said that the history of dementia praecox or schizophrenia is the history of psychiatry. This may be because the patients included in this group present the full complexity of human

life. The study of these serious cases is the study
of the tragi-comedy called life, and each individual case has its own unique character. No general
formula can do full justice to the particular circumstances of the individual case. General for-
mulae are dignified and diagnostic terms give
comfort, but they are verbal symbols which are
apt to do violence to the complexity of the facts.
Out of respect for the facts we may be shy of certain diagnostic terms, even though we thereby
deprive ourselves of a pleasing resting place.
Whoever fails to use the familiar verbal symbols
may be accused of diagnostic nihilism or of lack
of pious recognition of the labors of his predeces-
sors, who with unremitting toil constructed their
orderly schemata. One may seem to be a disturber
of the peace if one reject familiar diagnostic
terms, and if one insist that more important than
the formal diagnosis of the case is its formulation in terms of the familiar forces of human life,
based on the painstaking dynamic analysis of the
patient and his relation to the environment. With
such an outlook the neglect of conventional diagnostic terms may lead to some complaint from
our professional colleagues, but our patients at
least will not be able to reproach us with having
failed to do our best to understand the travail of

their spirit, their needs, and their goals, and to bring whatever relief is available to strengthen their bodies, reëstablish their personal equilibrium, restore them to their place in the social group. This was the spirit of the distinguished physician in tribute to whom these memorial lectures were established.

INDEX